The Bunkside Companion

Robin Knox-Johnston
with Ian Dear

STANLEY PAUL
London Melbourne Sydney Auckland Johannesburg

Stanley Paul & Co. Ltd

An imprint of the Hutchinson Publishing Group

17-21 Conway Street, London W1P 5HL

Hutchinson Group (Australia) Pty Ltd
30-32 Cremorne Street, Richmond South, Victoria 3121
PO Box 151, Broadway, New South Wales 2007

Hutchinson Group (NZ) Ltd
32-34 View Road, PO Box 40-086, Glenfield, Auckland 10

Hutchinson Group (SA) Pty Ltd
PO Box 337, Bergvlei 2012, South Africa

This selection first published 1981

Set in Linoterm Baskerville by
Book Economy Services, Cuckfield, Sussex

Printed in Great Britain by The Anchor Press Ltd
and bound by Wm Brendon & Son Ltd,
both of Tiptree, Essex

British Library Cataloguing in Publication Data

The Bunkside companion
1. Seamanship
I. Knox-Johnston, Robin
II, Dear, Ian
623.88   VK545

ISBN 0 09 146250 9

Contents

Acknowledgements

The editors would like to thank the following for permission to reproduce the extracts which appear in this anthology:

Alan Villiers, author of *Sons of Sinbad*, published by Hodder & Stoughton Ltd

Blond & Briggs Ltd, London, publishers of *Sacred Cowes* by Anthony Heckstall-Smith

George Harrap Ltd, publishers of *Great Sea Stories of All Nations*, from which 'T'Wind'ard!' by Captain David Bone is taken

Angus & Robertson (UK) Ltd, publishers of *The Yachtsman's Emergency Handbook* by Neil Hollander and Harald Mertes, and *Last But Not Least* by Robin Knox-Johnston

Nautical Publishing Co. Ltd, publishers of *Come Sailing Again* by Mike Peyton and *My Lively Lady* by Alec Rose

Anthony Heckstall-Smith, copyright holder of *All Hands on the Mainsheet* by Brooke Heckstall-Smith, published by Grant Richards Ltd

Granada Publishing Ltd, publishers of *Once Is Enough* by Miles Smeeton (originally published by Rupert Hart-Davis), and *Survive the Savage Sea* by Dougal Robertson (originally published by Elek Books Ltd)

The Bodley Head Ltd, publishers of *The Incredible Voyage* by Tristan Jones

Sheridan House, New York, publishers of *The Rudder Treasury*, in which 'Curious Records of the Sea' by Richard Maury appeared

Hodder & Stoughton Ltd, publishers of *Gypsy Moth Circles the World* by Francis Chichester

Introduction

When one considers the richness of the literature about the sea, it is very hard to have to choose only a few of the many favourites for an anthology. Ideally, of course, our boats would be large enough, and our passages long enough, to permit the stowage of all our favourite books, and the time to read them. But, for most of us, short trips are the norm, and there is rarely time for more than a quick dip into a book. Hence, this bunkside companion.

The pieces I've chosen have, for the most part, come from my own library, much of which has been collected over the years from various parts of the world. It took me a long time to track down *Sons of Sinbad*, and it was not until some years after I'd first heard of it that I found a copy in Mystic Seaport. I also had to look for the *Para Handy Tales* for ages before I found a copy on, of all places, Oban station. *Shark for Sale*, a particular favourite of mine, I happened to come across in Bahrein. On the other hand, I've collected C. S. Forester since I was eight. I read *Ship of the Line* first and then ended up with the complete library that was produced by Smith's at 4s 6d each. I still reread them from time to time with the same enjoyment.

Some of the books from which I've chosen extracts I was introduced to by that splendid organization the Seafarers Education Service, which provides libraries for merchant ships. Serving in the Merchant Navy – I was in the British India Steam Navigation Company for some years – certainly gave one the time to read as there was little else to do when off duty. So that was how I became acquainted with writers like Tilman, Bone and Chandler. However, when I was preparing for the round-the-world race in 1967 I decided to take only a few books on my favourite subjects, sailing and history. Instead, the Seafarers Education Service provided me with a splendid library consisting mostly of the classics. So as I ploughed my way through the Southern Ocean I devoured novels like *Tom Jones* and *Clarissa* – ideal reading for a long voyage, as it is five volumes long! – as well as books by Bertrand Russell (hard going) and Rachel Carson. The only one of the 120 I had on board that I did not finish was a weird one on parasitology, which I found altogether too obscure.

Nowadays, however, I don't read much at sea, especially when I'm racing. I like reading at bedtime, and when we moved to our present home in Scotland three years ago we put up five shelves in my study for my books. At the time they filled just one of the shelves. Now all five are full. This selection from them is necessarily arbitrary, and I have chosen them not just for their entertainment value but, in some cases, for their inspirational effect. Sometimes we want to laugh, sometimes to be distracted, and, sometimes, when everything is not going quite as well as we hoped, we need a little bit of a lift. So these extracts amuse, distract or inspire me, and I hope the reader will obtain the same enjoyment from them as I do.

Robin Knox-Johnston

ALAN VILLIERS

Nejdi's Race Home

(From *Sons of Sinbad*)

In the preface to one of his best-known books, The War with Cape
Horn, *Alan Villiers — who was born in Melbourne, Australia, in 1903
— wrote that he'd been doing his best to learn about deep-sea sailing ships
ever since he'd been capable of learning anything, and I'm sure he is one
of the great authorities on the different kinds of curious craft that are still
sailed in odd corners of the world. He is, perhaps, most famous for his
time in square riggers during the 1930s, but just before the Second World
War he spent a year with the Arabs sailing in dhows. Later, when he
wrote a book called* Sons of Sinbad *about these adventures, he said in
his introduction that the Arabs had difficulty in understanding why he
should bother to spend time with them in order to write a book on their
way of life afloat when they saw little of interest in such a life. I had no
such difficulty and I found* Sons of Sinbad *memorable reading. For
there is something about the way Villiers writes which grips the heart as
well as the mind, and he not only conveys his understanding and liking of
the Arabs amongst whom he lived during that year but he made me
understand and like them better too. I was so impressed with the
seaworthiness of the kind of craft Villiers wrote about that when I was
serving as Second Officer in a Persian Gulf-based passenger ship in 1962
I thought about building one and sailing it home when my tour was over.
I wrote to Villiers to ask his opinion. His reply was full of sound
suggestions and I took his advice and built a yacht instead. The extract
I've chosen is a chapter from near the end of the book which captures the
homeward bound atmosphere when the boom was on the last leg of her
voyage back to Kuwait. A boom, incidentally, is a type of dhow common*

12

*to that port. It is double-ended, has a straight-angled stempost built out
into a sort of planked bowsprit, and has yoke steering.*

Our dash homewards across the reefs from Bahrein to Kuwait
was the most dramatic episode of the voyage. Daylight the
morning after sailing showed that the other vessels were out of
sight and we sailed over a shallow sea through a fleet of pearlers –
tiny vessels full of men who, as we sailed by, were squatting
round their decks opening oysters. These were the fleet of
al-Qatif and Darien, Nejdi said, and they were greatly thinned
out by the depression. We hailed a few of them, asking what
luck they were having, but they replied only that Allah was
compassionate. Nejdi asked them also if they had seen any
other Kuwait deep-water men, but they said they had not.
Three or four had sailed several days before we did, but Nejdi
said none of these would dare to try this dash across the reefs.
The western side of the Persian Gulf from Bahrein almost to
Kuwait is littered with destruction, for coral reefs and banks
and shifting sands abound for 200 miles. Most of the area, being
of no interest to steamships, has never been properly charted,
but Nejdi had been pearling there since he was a child.

Every man in the ship knew those waters: there was none
among them who had not been sailing there at least ten years.
Nejdi knew every bank, every overflow, every low-sanded point.
We sounded frequently as we ran on, always with the lead
armed, though it had never been armed before. Some camel fat
was poked into a rough hole in the bottom of the lead, and Nejdi
examined with care the grit and shells and sand brought up on
this. He seemed able to follow our way in this manner, as
though he were reading signs on a city street. Sometimes we
weaved about leaving a wake behind us like the twistings of a
snake, though I could see no safe passage nor distinguish the
places where there were two fathoms of water from those where
there was only one.

We saw little of the land, for the Hasa coast is low, but Nejdi
seemed to know every inch of the water, every tiny craft we saw,

13

every minute variation of the gulf bed. This was native pilotage at its best and I watched him with envious interest. I could not have done this, not after ten years of pearling and sailing there, not with all the sextants and tables and chronometers and slide rules in the world. This was pilotage by eye and personal knowledge, almost by instinct. To navigate in this way a man must never clutter his mind with book learning: perhaps Nejdi was right, after all, in his scorn of our methods. Nejdi said that in this kind of work he was helped even by the colour of the sky, for he professed to detect a change in it over the shallowest places. What I found most amazing, however, was his apparent ability always to detect which way the sets were running and the tides, and to predict them. He had no tables and he did not even know the date. The moon, he said, was enough; the moon, the stars, and the behaviour of the sea.

We ran on that morning with the wind light and Nejdi impatient; for the first time in the voyage he was excited and craved speed. We had gone out with the second mainsail, not wishing to spread great Oud with the ship so lightly ballasted. A capful of wind in Oud could capsize her, with less than thirty tons of coral in the hold. But with our speed dropped to five knots Nejdi gave the order to lower the *sifdera*, as the second mainsail was called, and bend old Oud instead. This the sailors did with a will and Oud was aloft again faster than he had ever been before. No sooner was the great sail set than the wind freshened and we bowled along at ten knots in a welter of foam with the lee rail not far from the water. Let her go! Nejdi, crouching anxiously aft, watched her like an old sea eagle, and though she lurched now and again till it seemed that she must blow over, there was no sea and she ran on. She lay with a heavy list and the sea skimming past the lee side within inches of the rail, and the sailors laughed. Let her go! We gave her the mizzen and added the biggest jib, set on a spar lashed along the raked stemhead, and the breeze hummed in the rigging. The spray drove away before the bows and her wake ran behind for miles. The sea birds welcomed us, and the pearling fleet from Jubail looked up in astonishment as we raced by.

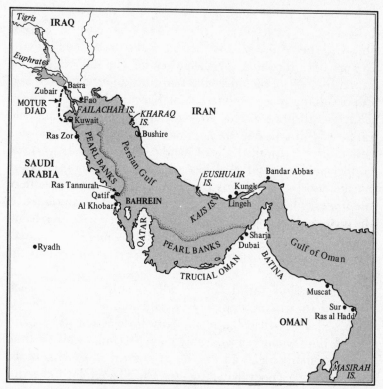

The Persian Gulf and the Gulf of Oman

We ran on through tide rips and across reefs where the bottom rose up alarmingly to bite at us; but Nejdi said there was water enough. We avoided the worst places. The quarter-masters not on wheel duty sounded continually with a handlead on each side, and their chanting of the depths sounded sweetly in the wind.

We saw nothing of the land but the gulf bottom and of that we saw enough. Once we saw the low spit of the point of Abu Ali, which was nothing but sand. All the Hasa coast beyond this brief glimpse of yellow sand was hidden in haze. All day we foamed and raced along and in the evening still kept all sail, though we were then in one of the most dangerous quarters of the whole Gulf. During the day the sailors had scrubbed the maindeck and the poop and cleaned their chests and all the brasswork. We raced onwards beneath the moon, a spotless ship with her white sails bathed in beauty and moonlit decks cleaner than they had ever been before. The sailors gathered round the bole of the mizzenmast wrapped in their cloaks and grinned happily and talked about Kuwait. Kuwait, Kuwait! That was all I heard. Kuwait, Kuwait! At last this paradise on earth was just below the horizon's rim and on the morrow would arise. Kuwait, Kuwait, where every ship was a sturdy clipper and every girl was beautiful, where the houses of the Sheikh and the merchants were mansions full of the wealth of the Indies, where the water was sweet and the fruit glorious and the melons lying upon the earth were flavoured with myrrh and honey. What a place this Kuwait must be – more fruitful than Zanzibar, more blessed than Beirut, more healthy than the Indian hills.

So the sailors raved, and Nejdi, squatting on his bench watching the driving ship, for once said nothing. Well, I should soon see. The patriotism of the Kuwaiti was not to be questioned, but I wondered what sort of town it could really be, from which so many men had to sail out in great ships most of the year, wresting a poor living from the sea. Though I wondered, I said nothing, for the enthusiasm of the group was infectious. Gone were all ills, even Ebrahim's fever, and little Jassim the cook hopped and skipped while Ismael, who a few days before had been suffering agonies of rheumatism, played merrily on his guitar. Sultan and the dying pearl diver Nasir spoke cheerfully of the girls they would marry the day after we came in, and Kalifa the helmsman smiled about his new baby. He had the best girl in all Kuwait, Sultan boasted. No, *he* had, said Zaid: and Saoud the little surly seaman said neither of them could have, for he had already married them all. Hassan the helmsman, coming forward after his trick at the wheel, spoke of his two wives waiting for him, both with child, one aged about twenty and the other, new last year, aged sixteen. He found he needed two, he said, in his brief summer at home after nine months at sea: one was not enough. Now he was looking forward to acquiring a third, for the two he had got along splendidly and were a delight in his life. With three it would be paradise. Two wives, he said – apart from the initial expense – cost no more than one: three would cost little more. The two he had were the best of friends and kept his little home spotless and pleasant always. He slept with one in the noon siesta, the other at night, in strict rotation, he said: there was no jealousy.

'If you will listen to an old man,' Yusuf said when Hassan had ended, 'you will consider long before you take this third wife. If you are so doubly blessed as to have found two women who will get along together and keep peace in your home, leave well alone, my son. For there are no three women on earth who can share one man; and the third may be a virago.'

'Oh moaner, thy wife is thirty!' Hassan rejoined and they all laughed at this joke. To say that a man has a wife aged thirty was to condemn him to the society of the ancient. But old Yusuf, though his wife might have been thirty, looked forward to seeing her and his home again no less than the others. Poor old fellow, his feet were in a dreadful state from the constant hardships of the voyage, lacerated on the jagged knots of the Rufiji poles, torn on the coral of Manama roads, bruised and battered by the heavy work. His feet, like those of all the sailors, were tough and tremendously hard: their soles were of calloused skin a quarter of an inch thick. Yet the coral and the pronged wood had broken through even this armour, and now his feet bled whenever he ran. I looked at them for him though he did not ask. There was little I could do except bathe them in boracic lotion and wrap them in adhesive tape, but my adhesive tape was all gone. No matter, Yusuf said, his wife would fix them up when he reached home. She understood how very well: she always fixed him up between voyages. I had a vision of old Yusuf in his little home in some back street of Kuwait, his little home with his three children, his herd of goats with their kids, and his chickens (for he had told me of these things), and being made ready for another voyage by the tender ministrations of his wife bathing his feet and anointing his eyes. Only the strength of his body could keep that little home going, and the pace in the Kuwait

17

ships is hard: no man receives favours. No man, that is, unless he is a musician of the standing of Ismael, who could bargain with *nakhodas* anxious to exhibit his talents down the African coast.

The pace in the Kuwait ships is dreadfully hard and the style killing. It must be especially hard on a man who has previously been pearl-diving. All jobs are rushed at, all orders obeyed on the run day and night, all sailors live on the sufferance of the *nakhoda* who, if he be impatient and overbearing, must still be put up with. Consideration for others is not a noticeable quality in the *nakhoda* class: life goes hard, I fear, with the old sailors. One who cannot stand the life drops out of it, I suppose: but usually he drops out in harness. There comes a day when he dies. The pace in the Kuwait ships is hard, foolishly hard, for there is no need for all this rush.

'It is our manner,' Nejdi said, not excusing or explaining it, but surprised that I should ask. The sailors themselves take pride in this rushing at all jobs, though some of them are often knocked down in the rush. It is a matter of pride to be first, to be the highest aloft, to pull the longest oar, to stow the heaviest poles. The Suri did not do it, or the Yemenites, or the Hadhrami, or the sailors from the Trucial coast and from Batina, or the Indians, or the Persians. It is the style of the Kuwait ships alone – smart, efficient and very impressive; but, I fear, also sometimes killing. I wondered how long old Yusuf would stand up to the rigours of his life, and what would become of his little home when he was ended. He spoke to me of a younger brother who had died in a boom at Karachi the previous year; it seemed to me that he would need the three-month rest in Kuwait between voyages. Not many sailors died ashore. Old Yusuf said it was the pearling that killed them, mostly, and he thanked God that he had to do that no more. His own small debt had been worked off for it was five years since he had been diving, and in all that time he had paid twenty rupees a year from his deep-sea earnings. With his debt gone, he was free. Compared with pearling, he said, even a month in the Rufiji loading mangrove poles was a holiday.

Next morning we still foamed on, for Nejdi had driven his ship without sleep or food through the night, squatting on his bench abaft the helmsman watching, watching, examining, in the binnacle's light, the sand and the shingle brought to him from the arming of the lead, sniffing at the wind. Sometimes we would fall off and change our course, this way or that, though I could see no reason. Nejdi said there were reefs, many of them. I knew that: it was how he knew where they were and how he found a channel between them, that baffled me. But he did. By mid-morning of the next day, storming past headland after headland, we were abeam of Ras Zor which marks the southern border of the city-state of Kuwait. The breeze freshened and Nejdi pointed to the land, murmuring 'Kuwait, Kuwait!' as if he could hardly believe that at last, after all these months, his homeland was again in sight. He called to me.

'Kuwait, Kuwait!' he said, pointing. 'There, there is a land of beauty for you to see! Do you not see that that is beautiful?'

'What, that piece of sand?' I asked, pretending to be unimpressed.

Nejdi looked horrified, though the coastline of Arabia in the neighbourhood of Ras Zor is in fact far from impressive, and none but the Kuwaiti would see much beauty in it.

'Sand! Piece of sand!' Nejdi almost shouted. 'Look at it, Nazarene! Here are no rough mountains, but the soft, low land, gentle as the swelling of a virgin's breasts. Are you not ashamed that you said the mountains of Oman were beautiful, those useless hills? Look now at this Kuwait!' And he looked himself, very long, and kept on looking, no longer caring whether I was impressed or not.

It looked very much like any other piece of sand and about as impressive as the Benadir coast south of Ras Haifun. But I did not say so, for I could see the emotion on Nejdi's dark face and the tears in his tired eyes. He had said during the night why he so drove his ship, with lee rail skimming the sea and the seams of great Oud splitting in the fresh south wind. He had heard at Manama that his favourite wife was in danger and might die.

Now we foamed by the islet of al-Kubbar, where the birds

rose in cloudlike flocks as we ran by, with the ship making perhaps twelve knots. We overhauled and sailed by the slow mail British India steamer which had left Bahrein when we did, carrying Nejdi's letter announcing his homecoming. We foamed by, and Nejdi showed the flag of Kuwait while the sailors laughed. The drums were warming at Jassim's fire, for the distance from al-Kubbar to Kuwait is less than twenty miles and we might be there in two hours. The sailors, in great excitement, rushed about getting out their best gowns and their most heavily blued headcloths, trimming their moustaches, cleaning their teeth. Some of them were too excited to do anything. Nejdi, with all dangers safely passed and only Kuwait before him (for al-Kubbar marked the end of the worst waters) made Hassan shave him and scrub him down, bathing him with water from the sea. After that, Yusuf perfumed him, and rubbed some Paris scent into his forehead and behind his ears, and searched through his chest to put the gold ornaments for his wives on top, handy for ļanding. Even the monkey, Yimid, joined in the excitement, hopping about and looking at the shoreline of Kuwait, while Bizz the Somali cat led her offspring Fahad, Farid and Fatima in a raid on the fire-box – when Jassim was not looking. The sea was very green there, and there was a white sand glare over the land (abeam and ahead), for we were close to the head of the Persian Gulf.

But when the wind dropped, steadily, and we sailed on slowly, taking the whole afternoon to make the twenty miles between al-Kubbar and Ras al-Ardh, the slow mail steamer passed us again, and this time we did not look. We picked up the low island of Failachah to the west'ard of Kuwait Bay. It was the last landfall. The voyage was done. It remained only to turn the corner, and anchor in Kuwait Bay. We saw the houses of Failachah and some sambuks on the beach, the water booms and the firewood booms, and the little belems coming down from Basra between Failachah and the mainland. We saw the tiny date-frond boats of the fishermen fishing in the sea of Ras al-Ardh, the fishermen sitting more in the water than out of it, for their boats are but bundles of water-logged reeds afloat, not

watertight or meant to be. We rounded the triangular beacon
on Ras al-Ardh and saw the light there flashing, as we stood in
for Kuwait Bay – slowly, now, very slowly, with the breeze
dying away and the tide against us.

With the last of the light we came in sight of the town of
Kuwait, with all our drums going and the decks full of song. We
came on slowly past the Sheikh's house. The night shut off the
view of the town as we came to it, and we came to our anchor in
darkness while the drum-banging and the singing went on and
on. We were forty-eight hours from Bahrein – fast mail time,
Nejdi said (though the slow mail beat us), and, though he had
driven his ship so splendidly home and brought his long and
difficult voyage to a successful conclusion, he was consumed
with disappointment because we arrived by night, and he was
robbed of his triumph. If we came by day the town would see us,
and boats full of his friends would come out to cheer and
welcome, and all the waterfront would know that Nejdi was
back again, up from Africa by way of Bahrein with a 'fast mail'
passage – Nejdi, the driver of ships and men, Nejdi with the
Triumph of Righteousness, triumphant over the seas again. It was a
blow to him to have no welcome, for we were unexpected and
his letter announcing our coming would not be delivered until
the morning.

The sailors still drummed and sang, but the sense of achievement was ended, temporarily, for Nejdi. The sails were lowered
and unbent for the last time this voyage, the sailors singing all
the time, singing praises to Allah and praise of Nejdi – singing,
singing, first as we came in under the shade of old Oud with his
fifty-nine cloths, and then at the anchorage under the stars.

ANTHONY HECKSTALL-SMITH

New York Yacht Club Cruise

(From *Sacred Cowes*)

Sherman Hoyt told me my favourite story about 'The King-fisher' (Grace Vanderbilt). The setting was Newport on a bright Sunday morning at the conclusion of the New York YC Cruise. Sherman was a guest aboard the commodore's great schooner, and as he waited to go ashore to church with his host and hostess, he strolled to and fro along *Atlantic's* spotless teak deck admiring the scene.

Newport was at its fashionable zenith and the anchorage off Rhode Island was crowded with splendid yachts. Sherman knew them all by sight. All, that is, but one. A large black ketch, lying a cable or so distant to starboard of *Atlantic*.

'I just couldn't put a name to her,' Sherman told me. 'I had seen her cross the starting line a bit late, her crew still hauling on the peak halyards as though her owner had only decided to join the cruise at the last minute. She looked old and a little shabby. Her professional skipper was at the wheel, and I remember spotting a couple of pretty girls in her cockpit.

'Since I hadn't sighted her again, I was surprised to find her lying alongside us the next morning,' Sherman went on. 'She was flying the club burgee and her owner's house flag, but as there wasn't a sign of life aboard her, I guessed they were all sleeping late, and I rather envied them. But church parade was the rule aboard *Atlantic* on Sunday morning at Newport, and there was no dodging it.

'The yacht's gig was alongside the gangway, and I and the

other guests were waiting with Grace. "Neilly" was late and Grace was tapping her prayer book impatiently. Then, just as he appeared on deck, a hell of a scream came from the black ketch, and out of her deckhouse shot a great big blonde. She was wearing only a nightgown and her long hair was flying in the morning breeze.

'As we all stared at her, she let out another piercing scream and shouted, "You're not ——— me again, you son-of-bitch!" Then, she jumped overboard.

'The moment she surfaced, she started yelling for help, and it was clear that she couldn't swim. So there was nothing for it but to send our gig to the rescue.

'I shall never forget what happened,' Sherman said, shaking with laughter. 'The bowman made a grab for her as she came up for the second time. She was a great big brute, and all the sailor succeeded in doing was to drag her nightgown over her head. She flopped back into the water as naked as a goddam mermaid, still yelling her head off.

'I suppose it took three of the gig's crew a good five minutes to haul her over the gunwale. But to me standing there on *Atlantic's* deck beside Grace, and trying not to laugh, it seemed more like fifty minutes.

'The blonde swore like a Marine. And to make matters worse, or better, depending how you looked at it, her boyfriend came upon deck. He was a huge bastard with a big black beard, stark naked, and still loaded. And he kept shouting to the crew to "let the double-crossing bitch drown".

'Grace was scarlet with rage and kept insisting that the commodore should have the owner of the black ketch – whoever he was – thrown out of the club.

'But we found out later the Black Beard wasn't even a member'!

CAPTAIN DAVID BONE

'T' Wind'ard!'

(From *Great Sea Stories of All Nations*)

This extract from a book called The Brassbounder *by Captain David
Bone relates how the captain of a sailing ship, in the days when as many as
six British ships a day were being lost in various parts of the world and a
place like the Lizard was littered with shipwrecks, ignores the advice of his
pilot when approaching a dangerous coastline. I like it because it describes
so well the occupational hazard faced by all masters of sailing ships as they
approached land. Any modern yachtsman will, I think, find this piece not
only an exciting read but a sobering one when he remembers that the men
the author writes about were obliged to sail large unwieldy vessels without
the benefit of the modern electronic navigational aids which fill his own
highly manoeuvrable, close-winded craft. A brassbounder, incidentally, is
an apprentice, the name deriving from the shining brass buttons all new
cadets wore on their jackets. Bone must have been one for he went to sea
early in life and made it his career. So he knew what he was writing about.*

For over a week of strong westerly gales we had kept the open
sea, steering to the north as best the wind allowed. A lull had
come – a break in the furious succession, though still the sea ran
high – and the Old Man, in part satisfied that he had made his
northing, put the helm up and squared away for the land. In
this he was largely prompted by the coasting pilot (sick of a long
unprofitable passage – on a 'lump-sum' basis), who confidently
asked to be shown but one speck of Irish land, and, 'I'll tell 'oo
the road t' Dub-lin, Capt'in!

24

Moderately clear at first, but thickening later, as we closed the land, it was not the weather for running in on a dangerous coast, ill-lighted and unmarked, but, had we waited for clear weather, we might have marked time to the westward until the roses came; the wind was fair, we were over-long on our voyage; sheet and brace and wind in squared sail thrummed a homeward song for us as we came in from the west.

At close of a day of keen sailing, the outposts of the Irish coast, bleak, barren, inhospitable, lay under our lee – a few bold rocks, around and above wreathed in sea mist, and the never-dying Atlantic swell breaking heavily at base.

'Iss, indeed, Capt'in! The Stags! The Stags of Broadhaven I tell 'oo,' said the pilot, scanning through his glasses with an easy assurance. 'Indeed to goodness, it iss the best landfall I haf ever seen, Capt'in!'

Though pleased with his navigation, the Old Man kept his head. 'Aye, aye,' he said. 'The Stags, eh? Well, we'll haul up t' th' wind anyway – t' make sure!' He gave the order, and went below to his charts.

Rolling heavily, broad to the sea and swell, we lay awhile. There was no sign of the weather clearing, no lift in the grey mist that hung dense over the rugged coastline. On deck again, the Old Man stared long and earnestly at the rocky islets, seeking a further guidemark. In the waning daylight they were fast losing shape and colour. Only the breaking sea, white and sightly, marked them bold in the grey mist-laden breath of the Atlantic. ' "Present themselves, consisting of four high rocky islets of from two thirty-three to three ought-six feet in height, an' steep-to," ' he said, reading from a book of sailing directions. 'Damme! I can only see three.' To the pilot, 'D'ye know the Stags well, mister? Are ye sure of ye're ground?'

'*Wel, wel!* Indeed, Capt'in,' Mr Williams laughed. 'I know the Stags, yess! Ass well ass I know Car-narvon! The Stags of Broadhaven, I tell 'oo. When I wass master of the *Ann Pritchard*, of Beaumaris, it was, always to the west of Ireland we would be goin'. Summer and winter three years, I tell 'oo, before I came to pilotin', an' there iss not many places between the Hull and

25

Missen Head that I haf nor seen in daylight an' dark. It iss the Stags, indeed! East, south-east now, Capt'in, an' a fine run to Sligo Bar!'

Still unassured, the Old Man turned his glasses on the rocky group. 'One – two – three – perhaps that was the fourth just open to the south'ard' – they certainly tallied with the description in the book – 'high, steep-to.' A cast of the lead brought no decision. Forty-seven! He might be ten miles north and south by that and former soundings. It was rapidly growing dark, the wind freshening. If he did not set course by the rocks – Stags they seemed to be – he would lose all benefit of landfall – would spend another week or more to the westward waiting for a rare slant on this coast of mist and foul weather! Already eighteen days from Falmouth! The chance of running in was tempting! Hesitating, uncertain, he took a step or two up and down the poop, halting at turns to stare anxiously at the rocks, in the wind's eye, at the great Atlantic combers welling up and lifting the barque to leeward at every rise. On the skylight sat Mr Williams, smiling and clucking in his beard that 'he did not know the Stags, indeed!'

'We haul off, pilot,' said stout Old Jock, coming at a decision. 'If it had been daylight . . . perhaps . . . but I'm for takin' no risks. They may be th' Stags, belike, they are, but I'm no' goin' oan in weather like this! We'll stand out t' th' nor' ard – "mainyards forward, mister" – till daylight onyway!'

Sulkily we hauled the yards forward and trimmed sail, leaving the rocks to fade under curtain of advancing night, our high hopes of making port dismissed. The 'navigators' among us were loud of their growling, as the ship lurched and wallowed in the trough of the sea, the decks waist high with a wash of icy water – a change from the steadiness and comfort of a running ship.

Night fell black dark. The moon not risen to set a boundary to sea and sky; no play of high light on the waste of heaving water; naught but the long inky ridges, rolling out of the west, that, lifting giddily to crest, sent us reeling into the windless trough. On the poop the Old Man and pilot tramped fore and aft, talking together of landfalls and coasting affairs. As they came and went, snatches of their talk were borne to us, the watch on deck – sheltering from the weather at the break. The Old Man's 'Aye, ayes,' and 'Goad, man's,' and the voluble Welshman's 'Iss, indeed, Capt'in,' and 'I tell 'oo's.' The pilot was laying off a former course of action. ' "... Mister Williams," he said, "I can see that 'oo knows th' coast," he said, "an' ... I 'oodn't go in myself," he said; "but if 'oo are sure –" '

'Brea-kers a-head!' – a stunning period to his tale, came in a long shout, a scream almost, from the lookout!

Both sprang to the lee rigging, handing their eyes to shield the wind and spray. Faint as yet against the sombre monotone of sea and sky, a long line of breaking water leaped to their gaze, then vanished, as the staggering barque drove to the trough; again – again; there could be no doubt. Breakers! On a lee shore!!

'Mawdredd an'l! O Christ! The Stags, Capt'in. ... My God! My God!'* Wholly unmanned, muttering in Welsh and English, Mr Williams ran to the compass to take bearings.

Old Jock came out of the rigging. Then, in a steady voice, more ominous than a string of oaths, 'Luff! Down helm m'lad, an' keep her close!' And the pilot, 'Well? What d'ye make of it, mister?'

'Stags, Capt'in! *Diwedd i!* That I should be mistake. ... The others ... God knows! ... If it iss the Stags, Capt'in ... the passage t' th' suth'ard ... I know it ... we can run ... if it iss the Stags, Capt'in!'

'An' if it's no' th' Stags! M' Goad! Hoo many Stags d'ye know, mister? No! No! We'll keep th' sea, if she can weather thae rocks . . . and if she canna!' A mute gesture – then passionately, 'T' hell wi' you an' yer b—y Stags: I back ma ship against a worthless pilot! All hands, there, mister – mains'l an' to'galn's'l oan her! Uup, ye hounds; up, if ye look fur dry berryin'!'

All hands! No need for a call! 'Breakers ahead' – the words that sent us racing to the yards, to out knife and whip at the gaskets that held our saving power in leash. Quickly done, the great mainsail blew out, thrashing furiously till steadied by tack

27

and sheet. Then topgal'n'sail, the spars buckling to overstrain; staysail, spanker – never was canvas crowded on a ship at such a pace; a mighty fear at our hearts that only frenzied action could allay.

Shuddering, she lay down to it, the lee rail entirely awash, the decks canted at a fearsome angle; then righted – a swift, vicious lurch, and her head sweeping wildly to windward till checked by the heaving helmsman. The wind that we had thought moderate when running before it now held at half a gale. To that she might have stood weatherly, but the great western swell – spawn of uncounted gales – was matched against her, rolling up to check the windward snatches and sending her reeling to leeward in a smother of foam and broken water.

A gallant fight! At the weather gangway stood Old Jock, legs apart and sturdy, talking to his ship.

'Stand, good spars,' he would say, casting longing eyes aloft. Or, patting the taffrail with his great sailor hands, 'Up tae it, ye bitch! Up!! Up!!!' as, raising her head, streaming in cascade from a sail-pressed plunge, she turned to meet the next great wall of water that set against her. 'She'll stand it, mister,' to the mate at his side. 'She'll stand it, an' the head gear holds. If she starts that!' – he turned his palms out – 'If she starts th' head gear, mister!'

'They'll hold, sir! . . . good gear,' answered the mate, hugging himself at thought of the new landyards, the stout Europe gammon lashings, he had rove off when the boom was rigged. Now was the time when Sanny Armstrong's spars would be put to the test. The relic of the ill-fated *Glenisla* now a shapely to'gallant mast, was bending like a whip! 'Good iron,' he shouted as the backstays twanged a high note of utmost stress.

Struggling across the heaving deck, the pilot joined the group. Brokenly, shouting down the wind, 'She'll never do it, Capt'in, I tell 'oo! . . . An' th' tide. . . . Try th' south passage. . . . It iss some years, indeed, but . . . I know. *Diwedd an'l!* She'll never weather it, Capt'in!'

'Aye . . . and weather it . . . an' the gear holds! Goad, man! Are ye sailor enough t' know what'll happen if Ah start a brace, wi' this press o' sail oan her? T' wind'ard . . . she goes. Ne'er failed me yet' – a mute caress of the stout taffrail, a slap of his great hand. 'Into it, ye bitch! T' wind'ard! T' wind'ard!'

Staggering, taking the shock and onset of the relentless seas, but ever turning the haughty face of her anew to seek the wind, she struggled on, nearing the cruel rocks and their curtain of hurtling breakers. Timely, the moon rose, herself invisible, but shedding a diffused light in the east, showing the high summits of the rocks, upreared above the blinding spindrift. A low moaning boom broke on our strained ears, turning to the hoarse roar of tortured waters as we drew on.

'How does 't bear noo, M'Kellar? Is she makin' oan't?' shouted the Old Man.

The second mate, at the binnacle, sighted across the wildly swinging compass card. 'No' sure, sir. . . . Th' caird swingin' . . . think there's hauf a p'int. . . . Hauf a p'int, onyway!'

'Half a point!' A great comber upreared and struck a deep resounding blow – 'That for yeer half a point' – as her head swung wildly off – off, till the stout spanker, the windward driver, straining at the stern sheets, drove her anew to a sea-ward course.

Nearer, but a mile off, the rocks plain in a shaft of breaking moonlight.

'How now, M'Kellar?'

'Nae change, sir! . . . 'bout east, nor'-east . . . deefecult . . . the caird swingin'. . . .'

The Old Man left his post and struggled to the binnacle. 'East, nor'-east . . . east o' that, mebbe,' he muttered. Then to 'Dutchy' at the weather helm, 'Full, m'lad! Keep 'er full an' nae mair! Goad, man! Steer as ye never steered . . . th' wind's yer mairk. . . . Goad! D'na shake her!'

Grasping the binnacle to steady himself against the wild lurches of the staggering hull, the Old Man stared steadily aloft, unheeding the roar and crash of the breakers, now loud over all – eyes only for the straining canvas and standing spars above him.

'She's drawin' ahead, sir,' shouted M'Kellar, tense, excited.

East, b'nor' . . . an' fast!'

The Old Man raised a warning hand to the steersman. 'Nae higher! Nae higher! Goad, man! Dinna let 'r gripe!'

Dread suspense! Would she clear? A narrow lane of open water lay clear of the bow – broadening as we sped on.

'Nae higher! Nae higher! Aff! Aff! Up hellum, up!' His voice a scream, the Old Man turned to bear a frantic heave on the spokes.

Obedient to the helm and the mate's ready hand at the driver sheets, she flew off, free of the wind and sea – tearing past the towering rocks, a cable's length to leeward. Shock upon shock the great Atlantic sea broke and shattered and fell back from the scarred granite face of the outmost Stag; a seething maelstrom of tortured waters, roaring, crashing, shrilling into the deep, jagged fissures – a shriek of Furies bereft. And, high above the tumult of the waters and the loud, glad cries of us, the hoarse, choking voice of the man who had backed his ship.

'Done it, ye bitch!' – and now a trembling hand at his old grey head. 'Done it! Weathered – by Goad!'

NEIL HOLLANDER AND HARALD MERTES

Constructing a Makeshift Sextant

(From *The Yachtsman's Emergency Handbook*)

The basic principle of a sextant is comparatively simple. However, in order to achieve the degree of accuracy required, the instrument has to be made to very high standards, as even a small error in the construction can lead to quite large error in navigation. Although all seamen have to know how to correct the basic errors, what happens if the instrument gets knocked overboard or damaged beyond repair? This is a method of making an emergency sextant which I think is quite ingenious, and which might just come in useful someday. I know it's possible to make your own sextant because a certain Fred Rebell once wrote a book, called Escape to the Sea, *in which he explained how he put together one from 'several pieces of hoop-iron; a boy scout telescope (price one shilling); an old hacksaw blade; and a stainless steel table-knife'! Incredibly, he not only managed to navigate across the Pacific, from Australia to Los Angeles, with this rudimentary instrument but did so in a Sydney Harbour 18-footer.*

MATERIALS

One piece of plywood or hardboard

Two pieces of mirror – approximately 2 × 3 cm each with a minimum of one straight edge

Two wooden blocks – approximately 2 × 3 cm

Two or three 5 cm strips of darkened photographic film, preferably the leader of a developed roll, or strips of dark plastic bag

One empty 35-mm film container, or an equal sized plastic bottle

One drawer handle

Five screws

20 cm dark-coloured thread.

PROCEDURE

Trace the scale on page 33, cut it out and glue it to the plywood

Drill the hole for the index arm pivot ■ 358

Using the template, cut the index arm from another piece of wood

Drill a hole in the centre of each of the two blocks, and glue a mirror to one side. These will become the index and horizon mirrors

Drill a small hole – pencil lead size – in the centre of the film container bottom, then glue it in place with its horizontal axis along the line ■ 355

Mount the horizon mirror ■ 356 with its *face* along the *45° angle* and its axis at point ■ 357

Mount the index mirror with its *face* over the *centre* of the index arm pivot ■ 358

Attach the index arm with a large screw, and tie one end of the thread around the screw. Glue or tie the other end to the lower tip of the index arm so that the thread passes the zero point on the compass rose and the zero point on the scale

Mount the handle on the back

Bend the film into slides or cut the plastic into strips and put as many as necessary over the mirrors. Tie in place with rubber bands or string

Adjust the index error by slightly changing the position of the thread

NOTE

The hole on the index mirror block should be slightly larger than the screw to allow for index error adjustment when the sextant is completed

Each mirror must be mounted at exactly 90° to the surface of the sextant

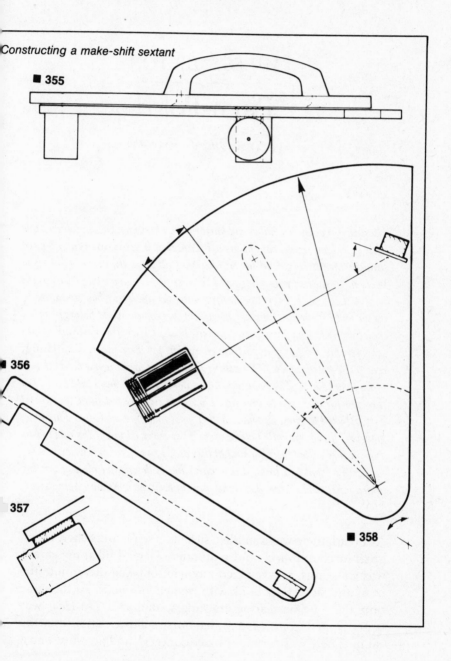

Constructing a make-shift sextant

■ 355

◼ 356

357

■ 358

MILES SMEETON

Pitch-Poled

(From *Once Is Enough*)

I can still vividly remember my horror at my first knockdown which came after a sudden squall caught me off Zanzibar in Suhaili. *Water poured through the skylight and my brother shot up from the cabin wanting to know what the hell was going on! I'll never forget that awful feeling as the boat heeled and then went on heeling until she was lying horizontal in the water and I wondered whether she would ever come upright before filling. I therefore read the Smeetons' famous book,* Once Is Enough, *with considerable sympathy as well as enjoyment for their yacht,* Tzu Hang, *was pitch-poled whilst approaching Cape Horn, a far worse effect than a plain knockdown. The boat was badly damaged and they could have been forgiven for deciding to give up. They didn't. They put in at the nearest port, effected repairs, and had another go at rounding the Cape. This time, however, they were rolled clean over. They survived to tell the tale but no wonder they called their book what they did! I've chosen their description of the first incident as I think it is a marvellously descriptive piece of writing which must send shivers down the spine of even the most unimaginative.*

As I read, there was a sudden, sickening sense of disaster. I felt a great lurch and heel, and a thunder of sound filled my ears. I was conscious, in a terrified moment, of being driven into the front and side of my bunk with tremendous force. At the same time there was a tearing cracking sound, as if *Tzu Hang* was being ripped apart, and water burst solidly, raging into the cabin. There was darkness, black darkness, and pressure, and a

34

feeling of being buried in a debris of boards, and I fought wildly to get out, thinking *Tzu Hang* had already gone. Then suddenly I was standing again, waist deep in water, and floorboards and cushions, mattresses and books, were sloshing in wild confusion round me.

I knew that some tremendous force had taken us and thrown us like a toy, and had engulfed us in its black maw. I knew that no one on deck could have survived the fury of its strength, and I knew that Beryl was fastened to the shrouds by her lifeline, and could not have been thrown clear. I struggled aft, fearing what I expected to see, fearing that I would not see her alive again. As I went I heard an agonized yell from the cat, and thought, 'Poor thing, I cannot help you now.' When I am angry, or stupid and spoilt, or struggling and in danger, or in distress, there is a part of me which seems to disengage from my body and to survey the scene with a cynical distaste. Now that I was afraid, this other half seemed to see myself struggling through all the floating debris, and to hear a distraught voice crying, 'Oh God, where's Bea, where's Bea?'

As I entered the galley, John's head and shoulders broke water by the galley stove. They may have broken water already, but that was my impression anyway. John himself doesn't know how he got there, but he remembers being thrown forward from where he was sitting and to port, against the engine exhaust and the petrol tank. He remembers struggling against the tremendous force of water in the darkness, and wondering how far *Tzu Hang* had gone down and whether she could ever get up again. As I passed him he got to his feet. He looked sullen and obstinate, as he might look if someone had offended him, but he said nothing. There was no doghouse left. The corner posts had been torn from the bolts in the carlins, and the whole doghouse sheared off flush with the deck. Only a great gaping square hole in the deck remained.

As I reached the deck, I saw Beryl. She was thirty yards away on the port quarter on the back of a wave, and for the moment above us, and she was swimming with her head well out of the water. She looked unafraid, and I believe that she was smiling.

'I'm all right, I'm all right,' she shouted.

I understood her although I could not hear the words, which were taken by the wind.

The mizzenmast was in several pieces, and was floating between her and the ship, still attached to its rigging, and I saw that she would soon have hold of it. When she got there, she pulled herself in on the shrouds, and I got hold of her hand. I saw that her head was bleeding, and I was able to see that the cut was not too serious, but when I tried to pull her on board, although we had little freeboard left, I couldn't do it because of the weight of her sodden clothes and because she seemed to be unable to help with her other arm. I saw John standing amidships. Incredibly he was standing, because, as I could see now, both masts had gone, and the motion was now so quick that I could not keep my feet on the deck. He was standing with his legs wide apart, his knees bent and his hands on his thighs. I called to him to give me a hand. He came up and knelt down beside me, and said, 'This is it, you know, Miles.'

But before he could get hold of Beryl, he saw another wave coming up, and said, 'Look out, this really is it!'

Beryl called, 'Let go, let go!'

But I wasn't going to let go of that hand, now that I had got it, and miraculously *Tzu Hang*, although she seemed to tremble with the effort, rode another big wave. She was dispirited and listless, but she still floated. Next moment John caught Beryl by the arm, and we hauled her on board. She lay on the deck for a moment, and then said, 'Get off my arm John, I can't get up.'

'But I'm not on your arm,' he replied.

'You're kneeling on my arm, John.'

'Here,' he said, and gave her a lift up. Then we all turned on our hands and knees, and held on to the edge of the big hole in the deck.

Up to now my one idea had been to get Beryl back on board, with what intent I do not really know, because there was so much water below that I was sure *Tzu Hang* could not float much longer. I had no idea that we could save her, nor, John told me afterwards, had he. In fact, he said, the reason why he had not come at once to get Beryl on board again was that he thought *Tzu Hang* would go before we did so. After this first action, I went through a blank patch, thinking that it was only a few moments, a few minutes of waiting, thinking despondently that I had let Clio down. Beryl's bright, unquenchable spirit thought of no such thing. 'I know where the buckets are,' she said. 'I'll get them!'

This set us working to save *Tzu Hang*.

Beryl slipped below, followed by John, but for the time being I stayed on deck and turned to look at the ruins that had been *Tzu Hang*. The tiller, the cockpit coaming, and every scrap of the doghouse had gone, leaving a 6 foot by 6 foot gap in the deck. Both masts had been taken off level with the deck, the dinghies had gone, and the cabin skylights were sheared off a few inches above the deck. The bowsprit had been broken in two. The rail stanchions were bent all over the place, and the wire was broken. A tangle of wire shrouds lay across the deck, and in the water to leeward floated the broken masts and booms – the masts broken in several places. The compass had gone, and so had the anchor which had been lashed to the foredeck.

There could be no more desolate picture. The low-lying, water-logged, helpless hull, the broken spars and wreckage, that greyish-white sea; no bird, no ship, nothing to help, except that which we had within ourselves. Now the sun was gone again, the spindrift still blew chill across the deck, and the water lipped on to it, and poured into the open hull.

I think both John and I had been numbed with shock, but he recovered first and was working in a fury now, and a hanging cupboard door, some floorboards, and the Genoa erupted on to the deck. I hung on to them, so that they would not be blown or washed off, while he went down again for his tools. He found his toolbox jammed in the sink, and when he groped under water for the tin of galvanized nails in the paint locker, he found them on his second dip. I had intended to help John, as the first essential seemed to be to get the hole covered up, but he was working so fast, so sure now of what he was going to do, his mouth set in a grim determination, oblivious of anything but the work in hand, that I saw he would do as well without me, and now Beryl, who was trying to bale, found that she could not raise the bucket to empty it. I climbed down to where Beryl was standing on the engine, the water washing about her knees. We had to feel for some foothold on the floor-bearers because the engine cover had gone. A 70-lb keg of waterlogged flour floated up to us.

'Overboard with it,' I said.

'Mind your back,' said Beryl, as if we were working on the farm.

I picked it up, and heaved it on deck, Beryl helping with her good arm, but it seemed light enough, and John toppled it over into the sea, out of his way. Anything to lighten the ship, for she was desperately heavy and low in the water.

'We'd better bale through the skylight,' Beryl said. 'I'll fill the bucket, and you haul it up. We'll need a line. Here, take my lifeline.' She undid her line from her waist and handed it to me, and I noticed that the snap-hook was broken. I tied it onto the handle of the plastic bucket.

We waded into the cabin feeling with our feet, because there were no floorboards to walk on. I climbed on to the bunk and put my head and shoulders through the skylight. Beryl was on the seat below with the water still round her knees. She filled the bucket and I pulled it up and emptied it, and dropped it down through the skylight again. It would have floated if she had not been there to fill it. It was the best that we could do, and although we worked fast, to begin with, we could just keep pace with the water coming in. No heavy seas broke over the ship, and when a top splashed over, I tried to fill the aperture with my body as best I could.

John was doing splendidly. He had made a skeleton roof over the hatch with the door and floorboards, and nailed it down, and he had made it higher in the middle, so that it would spill the water when the sail was nailed over. He was nailing the folded sail over it now, using pieces of wood as battens to hold it down. It was a rush job, but it had to be strong enough to hold out until the sea went down. As soon as he had finished he went to the other skylight and nailed the storm jib over it. Beryl and I baled and baled. As the bucket filled she called 'Right!' and I hauled it up again. Her voice rang out cheerfully from below, 'Right . . . Right . . Right!' and John's hammer beat a steady accompaniment. *Tzu Hang* began to rise slowly, and at first imperceptibly, in the water.

When John had finished with the skylight, he called to me to ask if he should let the rigging screws go, so that the broken spars would act as a sea-anchor. I told him to do so, and he then went round the deck and loosened all the rigging-screws, leaving only one of the twin forestays attached to the deck. He had not much to work with, as the topmast forestay and the jibstay had gone with the mast, the forestay had smashed the deck fitting, and the other twin forestay had pulled its ringbolt through the deck, stripping the thread on the ringbolt. All the rigging was connected in some way or other, so now *Tzu Hang* drifted clear of her spars and then swung round, riding head to wind, on her single forestay. This forestay was attached to a mast fitting on the broken mast, and the fitting was not equal to the strain now put on it, and it carried away. *Tzu Hang* swung away and drifted downwind, sideways to the sea, and that was the last that we saw of our tall masts, and the rigging, and the sails on the booms.

We baled and baled. We had two pumps on board, but the water that we were baling was filled with paper pulp from books and charts and labels. They would have clogged up with two strokes, and to begin with the pump handles themselves had been under water. John was now in the forecabin, standing on the bunks and baling through the skylight. Both he and Beryl were wearing the oilskins that they had been wearing when we upset, but I was still only in a jersey, and was beginning to feel very cold. I was continually wet with spray and salt water and lashed by the bitter wind, and my eyes were so encrusted and raw with salt that I was finding it difficult to see. A broken spinnaker pole rolled off the deck, showing that *Tzu Hang* was coming out of the water again, and was getting more lively. I saw a big bird alight by it and start pecking at it, and I supposed that this was also a sign that the wind was beginning to abate. I peered through rimy eyes to try and identify it, and saw that it was a giant fulmar. It was the first and only one that we saw.

After a time I became so cold that I could no longer pull up the bucket, in spite of Beryl's encouragement from below.

'This is survival training, you know,' she said.

It was the first joke. Survival training or no, I had to go below for a rest and we called a halt, and John came back from the main cabin and we sat on the bunk for a short time. Beryl found a tin of Horlicks tablets in a locker that had not been burst open, and she pulled off one of her oilskins and gave it to me.

'Where is Pwe?' I asked. 'Anyone seen her?'

'No, but I can hear her from time to time. She's alive. We can't do anything about her now.'

We were making progress, for the top of the engine was showing above the water. There was over a foot less in the ship already, and we were getting down to the narrower parts of her hull. We went back to work, and I found that now I had some protection from the wind the strength came back to my arms and I had no further difficulty. All through the day and on into the evening we baled, with occasional breaks for rest and more Horlicks tablets. Before dark, almost twelve hours after the smash, we were down below the floor-bearers again. After some difficulty we managed to get the primus stove, recovered from the bilge, to burn with a feeble impeded flame, and we heated some soup, but Beryl wouldn't have any. Now that the struggle was over for the time being, she was in great pain from her shoulder, and she found that she couldn't put her foot to the ground into the bargain. She had injured it stumbling about in the cabin, with no floorboards. Some blood-clotted hair was stuck to her forehead. Like a wounded animal, she wanted to creep into some dark place and to sleep until she felt better.

We found a bedraggled rag of a cat, shivering and cold, in the shelf in the bow, and with her the three of us climbed into John's bunk to try and get some warmth from each other.

'You know,' I said, 'if it hadn't been for John, I think that we wouldn't have been here now.'

'No,' he said. 'If there hadn't been three of us, we wouldn't be here now.'

'I don't know,' said Beryl. 'I think you were the man, the way you got those holes covered.'

'I think my toolbox having jammed in the sink, and finding those nails is what saved us, at least so far.'

Beryl said, 'If we get out of this, everyone will say that we broached, but we didn't. They'll say that there was a woman at the helm.'

'If they know you they'll say that's how they know we didn't broach, and anyway, we didn't: we just went wham. Let's leave it.'

'How far are we off shore, Miles?' John asked.

'About 900 miles from the entrance to Magellan I should say.'

'If we get out of this, it will be some journey. If there is a lull tomorrow, I'll fix these covers properly.'

'Get her seaworthy again, and get her cleaned up inside. I think that's the first thing to do.'

Beryl was restless with pain and couldn't sleep. In the end we went back to our own soggy bunks. As we lay, sodden and shivering, and awoke from fitful slumber to hear the thud of a wave against the side of the ship and the patter and splash of the spray on the deck, we could hear the main-sheet traveller sliding up and down on its horse. The sheet had gone with the boom, but the traveller was still there, and this annoying but familiar noise seemed to accentuate the feeling that the wreck was just a dream in spite of the water which cascaded from time to time through the makeshift covers. The old familiar noises were still there, and it was hard to believe that *Tzu Hang* was not a live ship, still running bravely down for the Horn.

For several days to come, although all our energies were spent in overcoming the difficulties of the changed situation, it seemed impossible to accept its reality.

W. S. GILBERT

The Yarn of the
Nancy Bell

'Twas on the shores that round our coast
   From Deal to Ramsgate span,
That I found alone on a piece of stone
   An elderly naval man.

His hair was weedy, his beard was long,
   And weedy and long was he,
And I heard this wight on the shore recite,
   In a singular minor key:

'Oh, I am a cook and a captain bold,
   And the mate of the *Nancy* brig,
And a bo'sun tight, and a midshipmite,
   And the crew of the captain's gig.'

And he shook his fists and he tore his hair,
   Till I really felt afraid,
For I couldn't help thinking the man had been drinking,
   And so I simply said:

'Oh, elderly man, it's little I know
   Of the duties of men of the sea,
But I'll eat my hand if I understand
   How you can possibly be

The Yarn of the Nancy Bell

'At once a cook, and a captain bold,
   And the mate of the *Nancy* brig,
And a bo'sun tight, and a midshipmite,
   And the crew of the captain's gig.'

Then he gave a hitch to his trousers, which
   Is a trick all seamen larn,
And having got rid of a thumping quid,
   He spun this painful yarn:

"'Twas in the good ship *Nancy Bell*
   That we sailed to the Indian sea,
And there on a reef we come to grief,
   Which has often occurred to me.

'And pretty nigh all o' the crew was drowned
   (There was seventy-seven o' soul),
And only ten of the *Nancy's* men
   Said "Here!" to the muster-roll.

'There was me and the cook and the captain bold,
   And the mate of the *Nancy* brig,
And the bo'sun tight, and a midshipmite,
   And the crew of the captain's gig.

'For a month we'd neither wittles nor drink,
   Till a-hungry we did feel,
So we drawed a lot, and accordin' shot
   The captain for our meal.

'The next lot fell to the *Nancy's* mate,
   And a delicate dish he made;
Then our appetite with the midshipmite
   We seven survivors stayed.

'And then we murdered the bo'sun tight,
   And he much resembled pig;

43

Then we wittled free, did the cook and me,
　　On the crew of the captain's gig.

'Then only the cook and me was left,
　　And the delicate question, "Which
Of us two goes to the kettle?" arose
　　And we argued it out as sich.

'For I loved that cook as a brother, I did,
　　And the cook he worshipped me;
But we'd both be blowed if we'd either be stowed
　　In the other chap's hold, you see.

' "I'll be eat if you dines off me," says Tom,
　　"Yes, that," says I, "you'll be," –
"I'm boiled if I die, my friend," quoth I,
　　And "Exactly so," quoth he.

'Says he, "Dear James, to murder me
　　Were a foolish thing to do,
For don't you see that you can't cook *me*,
　　While I can – and will – cook *you!*"

'So he boils the water, and takes the salt
　　And the pepper in portions true
(Which he never forgot), and some chopped shallot,
　　And some sage and parsley too.

' "Come here," says he, with a proper pride,
　　Which his smiling features tell,
" 'Twill soothing be if I let you see,
　　How extremely nice you'll smell."

'And he stirred it round and round and round,
　　And he sniffed at the foaming froth;
When I ups with his heels, and smothers his squeals
　　In the scum of the boiling broth.

'And I eat that cook in a week or less,
    And – as I eating be
The last of his chops, why, I almost drops,
    For a wessel in sight I see!

'And I never grin, and I never smile,
    And I never larf nor play,
But I sit and croak, and a single joke
    I have – which is to say:

'Oh, I am a cook and a captain bold,
    And the mate of the *Nancy* brig,
And a bo'sun tight, *and* a midshipmite,
    And the crew of the captain's gig!'

TRISTAN JONES

Hard Times

(From *The Incredible Voyage*)

*Tristan Jones is a Welshman who served in the Royal Navy until he was
wounded in a fracas with some guerrillas in Aden in 1952. But instead of
nursing his injuries and being content to live quietly on his pension he took
to small boat cruising which he has been doing ever since. He has written
four books so far about his adventures – and what extraordinary ones he's
had! The extract I've chosen is from his first book,* The Incredible
Voyage, *which I found compulsive reading. The title is in no way an
exaggeration, as it describes the task he set himself of sailing in the lowest
waters of the world and then the highest, a kind of vertical sailing record in
fact. The lowest, the Dead Sea (1250 feet down), he accomplished without
undue difficulty, but getting his yacht up to Lake Titicaca (12,500 feet up)
in South America was quite another matter. He succeeded in the end, but on
his first attempt he tried to get most of the way by sailing up the Amazon.
He got 1300 miles up that formidable piece of water but was then forced to
turn back. Reading this extract, which is about this part of the voyage,
makes it quite understandable why he did! I admire his pluck and his
unflagging zest for doing the unusual.*

The river craft of the Amazon are interesting. Down in the delta
there are many sailing craft. These are usually double-enders,
about forty feet long, flush decked, with one gaff sail and a small
headsail. At first sight they appeared to be crudely built, but
upon closer inspection we found that they were in fact very well
put together, considering that they are built by rule of thumb,

without the use of levels or, as far as I could see, any kind of measuring device. The Amazonian is a natural carpenter and shipwright, and it is a marvel to see him chopping away with only an adze, a tool which looks something like a sharp hoe, but with a very short handle. The timber they use is, of course, excellent – guaqui, a kind of teak, and ironwood, a very tough timber indeed, which they use for frames.

When *Barbara* entered Belém, not knowing the depths, she ran hard aground on the mud of Vero-Peso port. With the tide running out very fast there was nothing to do but prop her up until the next tide came in. Quickly Conrad swam ashore to collect balks of timber, of which there were many lying on the jetty. Scooping them up, he started throwing them in the water to float them over to the stranded boat. Most of them promptly sank, for they were ironwood. The locals howled with laughter at our ignorance!

From Belém up river most of the traffic is carried by strange-looking power craft called *yates*. These are sailing boat hulls, beautifully built and meticulously cared for, up to a hundred feet long, fitted with giant diesel engines, usually of Japanese make. A lot of the sailing gear and rigging is still carried, complete with very pretty ropework and bunting; and the boats are kept spotless, for the old Portuguese marine excellence shows through in the Brazilian.

Further upstream, beyond the rapid narrows of Obidos, beyond the farthest tidal point, sail completely disappears and we only saw *yates* and dugout canoes. These latter are a marvel of symmetry; the locals cut them out of a single log, by eye, in perfect form. They are propelled by one or two very broad-bladed paddles, which also serve to steer the craft. Because they are not very stable, however, it is quite an art to navigate a dugout, though we never once saw one capsize. Near the few towns the dugouts were equipped with small outboard engines. It was a peculiar sight to see one pass, loaded high with a whole family, some chickens, a pig, baggage, all shaded under big black umbrellas, on its way to market.

Soccer is almost a religion among the Amazonians, and we

would sometimes see a whole team, in complete playing gear, plus spectators, with flags and banners gaily flying and a band of musicians, paddling away in a group of dugouts, heading for a competitor's village.

At nightfall we headed into the bank to moor, for it is too hazardous to navigate in the dark. We sailed right up to an overhanging tree, secured a long line, then dropped out into the stream again to cast the anchor. We had to hold the boat out away from under the overhanging branches lest hordes of great ants, an inch and a half long, drop on board. These ants, the sauba, would have eaten the whole boat overnight! Also there was danger of snakes dropping on board. As it was, we used to paint the mooring line with kerosene to discourage them from slithering on board. Other dangers, if we stayed too near the shore, were jaguars, for they can leap long distances, and we didn't fancy making a meal for one of them!

While we were moored well out in the stream, floating islands would often come along and jam under the anchor line. Soon others would join that one, and if we were not lively we would have a hundred tons of Amazonian jungle bearing down on our anchor. As a result, we had to keep watches through the night, clearing the mass of vegetation away from the hull every hour or so. Up in the trees the howler monkeys made the most God-awful racket imaginable, screaming like tortured troglodytes.

After mooring to a tree we rigged up the mosquito net over the hatch and closed the hatch and all other openings into the hull; for as soon as the sun set, the onslaught of the mosquitoes began and continued with unabated fury, for about three hours, but sometimes all night. In the close, confined cabin, with all openings shut tight, it got very muggy. Every time one of us went topsides to clear the anchor line, a battalion of mosquitoes rushed in and set to work. Rubbing tobacco juice over any exposed skin helped to keep them away.

'Nasty little sods,' spat Conrad, as he beat them off.

'They can't hear you, you know,' I retorted. He grinned and remembered the Chinese trawler in the South Atlantic.

During the daytime, when the mosquito retired, the pium fly

took over. What a little monster! About a quarter of an inch in diameter, it is very black, almost like a horsefly. Beneath its ugly little body hangs a sack. It lands on exposed skin and sucks blood until the sack is about as big and red as a strawberry, then takes off, making a noise like a wet fart. There's no sting and, if you're not careful, in the course of a day you could bleed to death.

Vampire bats were a threat at night, too, but the mosquito net guarded against them. These ugly little devils hang upside down in the trees by the thousands. The face of the vampire bat must be the most evil-looking thing on earth. Sometimes they attacked in daylight, swooping down on the boat, fluttering straight into our faces, with malicious grins on their disgusting mouths, eyes glittering with wickedness. Conrad stood on the poopdeck swatting them with the cricket bat. Often he knocked up a score of a dozen or so, splattering their heads. Nothing like a good bit of English willow for a vampire bat! Some of them had a two-foot wingspan!

In the water were snakes and piranha fish. These latter are vicious, and can attack and consume a horse in a few minutes. Another danger is more subtle. It is a small fish, an inch long, which makes for the orifices of the body, usually the sex organs, and enters and penetrates into the urethra. There the little bastard opens a kind of hooking device. The only way he can be extracted is by operating, cutting the body open and lifting the little sod bodily out. We never once saw an Amazonian pissing in the river west of Manaus, and we were told that the reason is the little hook fish can actually swim up the piss stream and enter the penis orifice. Upon inspecting the hull intakes just before we emerged from the Amazon, we found thousands of the buggers, dead, in the engine intakes and cockpit drain hull fitting.

As *Barbara* slowly made her way upstream we had to use the engine more and more, in addition to every puff of wind. As we pushed along, the current got stronger and our speed less and less. By mid-April we were reduced to a crawl of no more than a knot. Our food stocks were low, we were now down to a sack of rice and a can of tea. There was not much time to fish, for all our energies were concentrated on making our way upstream. We were both suffering badly from malaria and loss of blood and lack of sleep caused by incessant insect attacks. However, we kept going, for our destination was upstream. On 25 April, our fuel supply was down to five gallons and this I determined to hoard against any future emergency. Our speed slowed to a mere crawl against the seven- and eight-knot current, though, when we had any wind, we would sail like blazes. Finally, just above the small, miserable settlement of Codajas, we started to *espia*, or haul the boat from one tree to the next. Soon we were covered with black scars left by the piúm fly, oozing pus, our bodies burned and dehydrated, but we kept going. First we took a 600 foot, 100 fathom nylon line upstream in the rubber dinghy (try rowing against a seven-knot current) to another giant tree crawling with six-inch-wide mygale spiders, and tied it to the tree. It was a two-man job, for these trees have a girth up to eighty feet around. Then we went back to *Barbara*, let go of the tree we were already tied to, and hauled her up to the next tree. And so on, for hours on end in the steaming heat. Sometimes we would see as many as a dozen sucuriju, water boa constrictors, fifteen feet long, hanging around waiting for a tasty morsel and sometimes the highly dangerous jararaca snake, whose bite can kill in less than three seconds.

'How's nature boy today?' I asked Conrad.

'Fascinating, isn't it?'

'Yes, like a bloody execution chamber!'

One of the few pleasant sights were the gorgeous butterflies, of which there are over 700 species in the Amazon. The biggest, the morphos, has a wingspan of a foot and is the prettiest insect I have ever seen, coloured a deep scarlet and gold. When the sun set, the yellow Amazon would turn a glittering gold colour. To see the emerald parakeets and the scarlet butterflies fluttering around in a deep azure sky at sunset almost made up for all the hardships.

Day after day we slaved at the *espia*, struggling with our remaining strength against the roaring waters of the Amazon.

Struggling in the stinking mist, across shoreside swamps, in the awful eternal smell of rotting vegetation, in the unceasing din of insects chirping, monkeys howling, trees crashing mightily, and always the river, the everlasting *brutal,* roaring current as it swooshed down thousands of miles to the Atlantic Ocean far away. Sick with malaria, our bowels scored with painful dysentery, scarred with running sores from pium bites, desperately in need of solid food, we pitted ourselves against the continent, with only the sailorman's will to fetch the destination keeping us alive and moving.

By 15 May, after sixteen days of hard slog, we had progressed exactly 160 miles. The river was rising by the hour, threatening to overflow the banks; already vast areas of the jungle were flooded. Soon, even the *espia* would not be possible, for we would be swept into some swamp and stranded there, rotting, dead, for ever. By now our main source of nutrition was to cut the rough bark from the cow trees and drink the thick, gooey liquid that oozed out, the colour and consistency of semen. Once we caught a manatee and boiled it in the pressure cooker. Another time we spotted a capybara, a huge rodent, about as big as a pig, eight feet long, and chased it downstream. After losing a hundred precious yards, we fell on it with a machete, harpoon, spear, and a hammer. We cut steaks off the huge, ratlike, hairy monster and ate them voraciously. We knocked a cebidae monkey off a high branch and, finding him very skinny under the fur, cut off his arms and boiled them. The sight of his shaven arms sticking out of the pot, with hands like those of a newborn baby, will stay with me the rest of my life. He had another hand on the end of his tail, for grasping the high branches. We didn't eat his tail, though we were tempted.

The fight to keep the sauba ants off the boat was everlasting. These ants are insatiable and will eat anything organic, including wood. They are so powerful, I was told, that on one occasion at least they were known to have dug a tunnel under a river as broad as the Hudson off Manhattan in order to get at the vegetation on the other side! The only sure way to get rid of them, once they establish a foothold, is to blow them up with gunpowder or burn them with gasoline. Of course, neither of these solutions was practical on board *Barbara*, so we tethered four chameleons on a long line, topsides. These lizards, about eight inches long, with great long tongues, flicked up the ants as they climbed or dropped on board. They were well fed and we were safe from ants.

Our trailing lines were a nuisance, continually getting tangled in vegetation. We caught tucunaré, a pretty fish, with an eyelike spot on its tail and good eating; but we had to be careful, for there are stingrays in the Amazon, a wound from which, in our weakened condition, might have killed us.

As slow as a wet Sunday, we crept up against the rushing waters. Then, on 20 May, we finally came to a halt. The scene was morbid. We tied up by the rotting wooden crosses of an old-time rubber-collectors' graveyard, now overgrown by the conquering jungle, alive with mosquitoes and piúms, and held a council of war.

This is the custom of sailormen when there are vital decisions to be made, when there are valid alternatives, each one of which might be fatal. All the cards are put on the table, all the bullshit discarded, and the odds are carefully and honestly calculated.

With aching hearts, after an hour's argument, we both conceded that we had lost this round. The Amazon had beaten us. We would have to turn back. This was the most painful decision I had ever made, for in twenty-five years of voyaging in small craft I had never failed to reach my destination except once, when dismasted off Greenland in 1962. We had pitted our puny craft against the wildest continent in the world, and we had lost. All the hard sailing across half the world, all the risk-taking up fourteen hundred miles of the uncharted Amazon, all the suffering – the heat, the loss of blood, the grinding effort, hard physical and mental effort, the hunger – all the discomfort and isolation from the civilized world, all the wear and tear on the boat and her gear, had been to no avail. The Amazon had beaten us.

'Well, if he isn't lost we are.' (From *Come Sailing Again* by Mike Peyton)

Southern Ocean Hot Toddy Recipe

This recipe is very good for colds, or when cold. It is a drink I 'developed' when sailing through the Southern Ocean on my own in Suhaili. *We kept running into thick fog, and the water temperature was very low which, of course, hinted at the presence of icebergs. The result was that I spent long hours keeping a lookout from the cabin, with my head stuck up out of the hatch. After a few hours my sinus began to ache intolerably so I kept myself warm by making hot drinks, and this particular recipe became a favourite. After I got back and met Sir Alec Rose, I discovered that he had used an almost identical formula.*

Take a pint tankard and put in two dessertspoons of sugar.
Cover with brandy. Mix in one dessertspoon of honey.
Add half a lemon sliced, and mix thoroughly.
Top up with boiling water, mixing all the time.

FRANCIS CHICHESTER

Rounding the Horn

(From *Gypsy Moth Circles the World*)

Francis Chichester took up sailing seriously quite late in life, having established a world-wide flying reputation in the 1930s. He won the first single-handed trans-Atlantic race in 1960 at an age when most men are thinking about their pensions, and that success seemed to spur him on to greater things, culminating in his magnificent one stop circumnavigation in 1966–67. It was this achievement that inspired me – and others – to try and do what he made obvious was the only thing left to do – sail round the world nonstop. I first met him in 1969, just after I got back from the round-the-world race, and we got on very well together. He was an amazing man, tough, fit, shrewd, a bit cunning, and a very good and interesting friend. I think what he did during his lifetime is an example for all of us. From his book, Gypsy Moth Circles the World, *I've taken his description of his rounding the Horn – which, like me, he obviously found less horrific than its reputation made it out to be – because what he has to say about this part of his trip is typical of the man and his attitude to things – irascible, perhaps, but what an individualist!*

When I was researching in records and old logs in preparation for my voyage it was soon apparent that the seas around Cape Horn had a reputation unique among all the oceans of the world; more, they have had this reputation for as long as man has known them, ever since Drake deduced that there was the passage that bears his name between Cape Horn and the South Shetland Islands off Antarctica – Drake Strait.

Cape Horn is an island, or rather the tip of an island, a massive cliff some 1400 feet high that stands where the Pacific and Atlantic Oceans meet, at the southerly end of the South American continent. Why has it such an evil reputation? I tried to answer this question in my book *Along the Clipper Way*.

The prevailing winds in the Forties and Fifties, between 40° S and 60° S, are westerly and pretty fresh on the average. For instance, off the Horn there are gales of force 8 or more on one day in four in the spring and one day in eight in the summer. Winds have a lazy nature in that they refuse to climb over a mountain range if they can sweep past the end of it. South America has one of the greatest mountain ranges in the world, the Andes, which blocks the westerlies along a front of 1200 miles from 35° S right down to Cape Horn. All this powerful wind is crowding through Drake's Strait between Cape Horn and the South Shetland Islands, 500 miles to the south. The normal westerlies pouring through this gap are interfered with by the turbulent, vicious little cyclones rolling off the Andes. The same process occurs in reverse with the easterly winds which, though more rare than the westerlies, blow when a depression is passing north of the Horn.

As for the waves, the prevailing westerlies set up a current flowing eastwards round the world at a mean rate of 10 to 20 miles per day. This current flows in all directions at times due to the passing storms, but the result of all the different currents is this 10 to 20 miles per day flowing eastwards. As the easterly may check this current or even reverse it for a while, the prevailing stream flowing eastwards may sometimes amount to as much as 50 miles a day. As with the winds, this great ocean river is forced to pass between South America and the South Shetland Islands. This in itself tends to make the stream turbulent.

But there is another factor which greatly increases the turbulence. The bottom of the ocean shelves between the Horn and the Shetland Islands and this induces the huge seas to break. It is like a sea breaking on the beach at Bournemouth in a gale, except that the waves, instead of being 4 feet high, are likely to be 60 feet high.

There is yet another factor to make things worse. Anyone who has sailed out past the Needles from the Solent when the outgoing tide is opposing a force 6 wind knows what a hateful short steep sea can result. A yacht will seem to be alternately standing on its stem and its stern with a lot of water coming inboard. The same thing happens at the Horn on a gigantic scale if there is an easterly gale blowing against the current flowing past the Horn.

What size are these notorious waves? No one yet has measured them accurately in the Southern Ocean, but the oceanographers have been measuring waves in the North Atlantic for some years. The British Institute of Oceanography have invented a wave measuring instrument which they use at the weather ships stationed in the Atlantic. Recently one instrument with a 60-foot scale recorded a wave of which the trace went off the scale. This wave was estimated at 69 feet in height, higher than our five storey house in London. An American steamship in the South Pacific is said to have encountered a wave 112 feet high. Brian Grundy who used to sail with me in *Gipsy Moth II* told me that when he was in the Southern Ocean in a big whaling steamer he reckoned that one wave was 120 feet high. L. Draper of the Institute of Oceanography says that, according to *Statistics of a Stationary Random Process,* if a sea of average height 30 feet is running, then one wave out of every 300,000 can be expected to be four times that height, i.e. 120 feet.

I do not think that Drake himself ever saw Cape Horn. We have two accounts of his passage, one by his chaplain in the *Golden Hind,* Francis Fletcher, the other by a Portuguese pilot, Nuno da Silva, whom Drake had captured with a ship he took off the Cape Verde Islands earlier in his voyage. Apparently da Silva accompanied Drake quite willingly for the sheer interest of adventuring into the unknown South Sea, for when Drake freed his other captives da Silva stayed with him. Piecing together Fletcher's and da Silva's accounts, and deducing Drake's navigation from them, I am convinced that Drake never rounded Cape Horn. He was driven west-south-west for fourteen or twenty-one days (the accounts are indefinite about the length of time), he then sailed back over his track for seven days as soon as the north-east gale had blown out. He fetched up at the Diego Ramirez Islands, where he anchored in 20 fathoms at the range of a big gun from the land. According to the *Admiralty Pilot* there is an anchorage close eastward of the middle of one island in a depth of 16 fathoms with a sandy bottom. I am convinced that Drake never saw Cape Horn, but discovered the

Diego Ramirez Islands and correctly deduced because of the big swell that rolled in from the Atlantic when the north-easterly gale was blowing, that there was a passage between the Atlantic and Pacific Oceans there.

I aimed to pass between the Diego Ramirez group and the Ildefonso islands, and to round Cape Horn between 40 and 50 miles south of it. I wanted to give the Horn a good clearance, because it is a bit like Portland Bill in the English Channel – the closer to the Bill you pass, the more turbulent the sea, especially with wind against tide. The water diverted by the Bill has to accelerate to get past it, and, in addition, the bottom shelves, so that the current is accelerated again because of the same amount of water having to get through where there is only half the depth. It is exactly the same case with the Horn, only the rough water extends 40 miles south of it, instead of 6 miles and where a 40-knot wind would bring a turbulent, 6-foot sea by the Bill, it will be an 80-knot wind with a 60-foot sea off the Horn.

At midnight on Saturday–Sunday, 18–19 March, I was approaching land. I was 134 miles from the Ildefonso Islands and 157 miles from the Diego Ramirez Islands. The nearest land was at the entrance to the Cockburn Channel, which Joshua Slocum had made famous. That was only 75 miles to the NE by N. The barometer had been dropping steadily for forty hours now. I got up and went into the cockpit to find out what chance I might have of sighting land ahead. It was raining steadily. The big breaking seas showed up dazzling white with phosphorescence, I would say up to 100 yards away. The falling-off, seething bow waves were brilliant white. The keel was leaving a weaving tail like a comet 50–100 feet long, and under the surface. I thought that one would be lucky to sight land 300 yards ahead. This would pose a nutty problem for me next night if I didn't sight any land during the day. If the weather continued I should be lucky to get a fix, and with the strong currents known to be there, my fix of the day before would not reassure me much. I was uneasy about fixes with no checks since Sydney Heads: suppose I had been making a systematic error in my sights. . . . But it was no good thinking like that. I realized that I must trust my navigation as I had done before.

I was lucky, and I got a sun fix at 09.22 next morning. That put me about 40 miles south-west of the nearest rocks off Tierra del Fuego. I was 77 miles due west of the Ildefonso Islands, and 148½ miles from Cape Horn.

There was a massive bank of cloud, nearly black at the bottom, away to the north, and I supposed that it was lying on the Darwin Mountains of Tierra del Fuego. There was no land in sight although the nearest land was only 50 miles off. I now had a big problem to solve – where should I head? My then heading of 78° would lead me to Duff Bay and Morton Island, 15 miles north of the Ildefonsos. But I could gybe at any time, because the wind had backed to west by north. My main problem was this: if I kept headed for the Ildefonso Islands and Cape Horn, which was nearly in line with them, I should reach the islands in eleven hours' time, i.e. at 22.00 that night, which was three and a half hours after dark. This was too risky, because if it rained or snowed I should be unable to see the islands close to. The trouble was that if I bore away from the Ildefonsos, I should then have to cope with the Diego Ramirez Group. The bearing of that batch of rocky islets was only 22° (2 points) to starboard of the Ildefonsos. These islands have no lights, and are inhabited only for part of the year.

It was clear that I should not reach the islands until after dark. The currents were strong here in the neighbourhood of the Horn, running up to 22 miles per day in any direction in fine weather, and up to 50 miles a day in stormy weather. My fix of 09.30 that morning seemed a good one, but at the back of my mind was still the gnawing doubt about my sun navigation, with no check since Sydney Heads, 6575 miles back. (It was unfortunate that I had made that blunder in my sun fix earlier, on the day before I appeared to have made the big 217 miles day's run.) I could avoid both groups of islands by gybing and heading south-east till dawn; that was safe tactics, but it meant quite a big detour, which I resented. I tried to puzzle out a dog's leg route which would take me between the islands in safety.

At noon the wind shifted, veering suddenly, which put me on a heading of north-east, so I gybed. Then the sun showed through the heavy clouds, and I got a sextant sight. This checked my latitude, for which I was very grateful. I had just finished plotting the result, and had decided on my best heading, when the wind backed in a few seconds from north-west to south. In a matter of minutes it was blowing up to a strong gale, force 9. I dropped the mainsail, the jib and the genny staysail in turn. I set the spitfire, and found that was enough sail. 'I wish,' I logged, 'that this famous visibility following a wind shift would prove itself! I should just love to get a glimpse of those islands.' Until then I had been heading straight for the Ildefonso Islands, and now I decided that the time had come to change course and head midway between the two groups of islands. This put the wind slightly forward of the beam; so I hoisted a storm staysil with the spitfire jib. The barometer had suddenly risen 6½ millibars in the past hour or two. I hoped that the wind would not go on backing into the south-east, which would make it very awkward for me. By 21.00 that night the wind had eased to 15 knots at times, but with periodic bursts of up to 36 knots. I hoisted a bigger staysail, but with only the two headsails set the speed was down to 4 knots between the squalls. I decided to put up with this until I had got away from the proximity of that rugged land, so notorious for williwaws.

By midnight the barometer had risen 9½ millibars in the past seven hours. It was a little less dark out: I could tell the difference between sea and sky.

If my navigation was all right, I should be now passing 18 miles south of the Ildefonso Islands, and at dawn I should be passing 12 miles north of the Diego Ramirez group. It was so dark that I did not think it worth keeping a watch, so I set the off-course alarm to warn me if there was a big wind shift, and I also set an alarm clock to wake me at daybreak. Then I put my trust in my navigation and turned in for a sleep. For a while I lay in the dark with the boat rushing into black night. I used to think I would be better off going head first into danger (in *Gipsy Moth III* I lay feet forward); but I still had the same fear. What would it be like if she hit? Would she crack with a stunning shock and start smashing against the rocks in the breakers? If I could reach the life raft amidships could I get it untied in the dark, then find the cylinder to inflate it? In the end I slept, and soundly too.

Daybreak was at 05.00. It was a cold, grey morning. The wind had veered right round again to west by south, and the barometer was steady. There was nothing in sight anywhere, which was as it should be. The sea was pretty calm, so I decided to head directly for Cape Horn, instead of passing 40 miles to the south of it as I had planned earlier, in order to avoid the turbulent seas to be expected if closer to the Horn, and if a gale blew up. I decided to hoist the trysail and went on up to do so. I was excited about changing course to east by north after setting the trysail, because changing course northwards there meant changing course for home. I was then 40 miles from the Horn.

When I stepped into the cockpit I was astounded to see a ship near by, about a half-mile off. I had a feeling that if there was one place in the world where I would not see a ship it was off Cape Horn. As soon as I recovered from the shock I realized that because of its drab overall colour it must be a warship, and therefore was likely to be HMS *Protector*. On first sighting it, it had seemed like magic, but on thinking it over I realized that if they had picked up my radio message to Buenos Aires of the night before relating how I was aiming to pass midway between the two groups of islands sailing blind during the night, the warship had only to place herself halfway between the two groups, and if my navigation was correct I should sail straight up to her. I went below and called up HMS *Protector* on 2182 kcs. She answered immediately. I said I would speak to her again as soon as I had set my trysail.

After setting the trysail I went down below for quite a while. I talked to *Protector*, and that used more time than it should have done, because I had great difficulty in hearing what her operator was saying. This was tantalizing because I could clearly hear some land stations up to 7000 miles away if I wanted to. After that I had my breakfast, and did not hurry over it, then wrote up the log, studied the chart and decided on my tactics, etc. While I was breakfasting a big wave swept over the boat and filled the cockpit half full. It took more than fifteen minutes to drain. By the time I had finished breakfast the wind had risen to 40 knots. At 09.00 I went on deck, and dropped both the trysail and the genoa staysail, leaving only the spitfire set. As I was finishing the deckwork a big wave took *Gipsy Moth* and slewed her round broadside on; in other words she broached to. It was lucky that I was on deck to free the self-steering gear, and to bring her round onto course again. I stood on the cockpit seat to do this so as to keep my legs out of the water in the cockpit. I looked round and there was the Horn, quite plain to see. It stood up out of the sea like a black ice-cream cone. Hermite Island, north-west of it, was grey and outlined against the sky.

At 10.43 I logged:

I reckon I am east of Old Horn, but I can't get a bearing without going into the cockpit. Perhaps I had better, as I have kept all my oilskins on. Still gusting over 50 knots.

At 11.15 I took a bearing of the Horn and was then definitely past it. As I had made good 39 miles in the past five and a quarter hours, a speed of 7.4 knots, I must have passed the Horn at 11.07½ o'clock. I had no time or inclination at that moment, however, for such niceties of navigation. Before I reached the Horn the familiar quiet roar of wind was beginning; it was blowing up, and the sea was roughing up fast. I dare say that a lot of this was due to being only 7½ miles south of the Horn when I passed it. I was beginning to feel seasick, and had the usual lethargic reluctance to do anything. I just wanted to be left alone, by things and especially by people. I cursed the *Protector* for hanging about, especially as I noted that she looked steady enough to play a game of billiards on her deck.*

---

* Apparently it was not as smooth aboard her as it appeared. A Reuter staff man, Michael Hayes, was aboard and recorded the following (published in a special issue of *Football Monthly*): 'As I stood on the pitching and tossing deck of the Royal Navy Ice Patrol ship HMS *Protector* 400 yards off, the sight was awesome. The translucent, bottle-green seas were moving mountains and valleys of water, rearing, rolling and subsiding with a fearful brute force. The 50-mile an hour wind slashed at the waves,

Just then I'm damned if an aircraft didn't buzz into sight. I cursed it. If there was one place in the world where I expected to be alone it was off Cape Horn; besides which this aircraft made me apprehensive. I couldn't say exactly why, but I think that an old flier has a perception which amounts almost to instinct about an aeroplane in flight. I thought this one would come down and crash into. the water. How the devil was I going to attempt the rescue of its occupants in that sea? I tried to figure out a drill for rescue. Queasiness made it hard to think, and I was greatly relieved when it finally cleared off.*

Ten minutes after noon I logged: 'I tried to be too clever (as so often, I regret). I went out to try to coax *Gipsy Moth* to sail more across the wind; the motive being to get north into the lee

slicing off foaming white crests and sending icy spume flying. Lead-grey clouds, blotting out the weak sun on the horizon, rolled across the sky, so low that it seemed I could reach up and touch them. The thermometer said the temperature was 43° F, but the numbing wind cut through my lined, Antarctic clothing like a knife, and salt spray swelled up and crashed against the face with stinging fury.'

* This was the aircraft, a Piper Apache, in which Murray Sayle of the *Sunday Times*, Clifford Luton and Peter Beggin of the BBC came out to look for *Gipsy Moth*. It was piloted by Captain Rodolfo Fuenzalida, formerly of the Chilean Air Force. Murray Sayle wrote in *The Times* of March 21:

'The flight out to find and photograph him at the most dangerous point of his voyage was a magnificent and terrifying experience. I flew from Puerto Williams, the tiny Chilean naval base which is the southernmost inhabited spot in the Americas.

'As my aircraft rose to find a cleft in the mountains of Hoste Island, the biggest of the Horn group, I was confronted with a superb sight. Green glaciers tumbling from the high snow-blanketed Darwin ranges into the Southern Ocean. As I flew by Cape Horn Island, its grey pyramid could be seen lashed by heavy seas and rimmed by breaking seas which appeared from time to time through the driving rain.

'South of the Horn the waves were driving eastward in long ridges of white and grey-green. Overhead were black driving clouds driven by the gale and a mile or two ahead the clouds were joined to the sea by rain in a black, impenetrable barrier towards the south and the pole.

'I picked up HMS *Protector* first, wallowing in the heavy seas as she kept company with the yacht. Then I picked out the salt grimed hull of *Gipsy Moth* lurching forward as the seas passed under her. My Chilean pilot, Captain Rodolfo Fuenzalida, gamely took us down to 60 ft where spume torn from the seas lashed across the aircraft's windscreen. But I had time to pick out Chichester in his cockpit, apparently nonchalantly preparing for his change of course and the long voyage home.

'When my pilot waggled his wings in salute we were rewarded by a wave of greeting. "Muy hombre," said the pilot, which I freely translate as "What a man."

'On the flight home we had severe turbulence as we threaded our way back through the mountains, and we lost an engine over the Strait of Magellan. It was a flight I am not too anxious to repeat, but the sight of *Gipsy Moth* ploughing bravely through this wilderness of rain and sea was well worth it.'

of land.' I thought that if only I could make some northing, I would get protection in the lee of Horn Island, and the islands to the north of it. However, the seas did not like it when I started sailing across them, and a souser filled the cockpit half full when I was in it. As a result, I had to change all my clothes, and also put *Gipsy Moth* back onto her original heading. That kept me just on the edge of the wind shadow from Cape Horn, and that might have made for more turbulence.

However, the wind was backing slowly, so that I steadily approached the heading I wanted to Staten Island. Unfortunately, with the wind shifting into the south-west, I got no protection whatever from the land, and after *Protector* left (one and a half hours after noon) the seas built up to some of the most vicious I had experienced on the voyage.

When *Protector* forged ahead, turned round ahead of *Gipsy Moth* and went away, she left me with a forlorn, empty feeling of desolation. I think it is a far greater strain to have a brief sight of a ship full of people in such conditions than it is to be quite alone: it emphasizes the isolation, because it makes one realize the impossibility of being helped should one require help. The odd thing was that I had not only no feeling of achievement whatever at having passed the Horn, but I had no more feeling about it than if I had been passing landmarks all the way from Australia.

The Eddystone Light

Me father was the keeper of the Eddystone Light,
He married a mer-my-aid one night;
Out of the match came children three—
Two was fish and the other was me.

> Jolly stories, jolly told
> when the winds is bleak and the nights is cold;
> No such life can be led on the shore
> As is had on the rocks by the ocean's roar.

When I was but a boyish chip,
They put me in charge of the old lightship;
I trimmed the lamps and I filled 'em with oil,
And I played Seven-up according to Hoyle.

One evenin' as I was a-trimmin' the glim
An' singin' a verse of the evenin' hymn,
I see, by the light of me binnacle lamp
Me kind old father lookin' jolly and damp;
An' a voice from the starboard shouted 'Ahoy!'
An' there was me gran'mother sittin' on a buoy—
Meanin' a buoy for ships what sail
An' not a boy what's a juvenile male.

> Jolly stories, jolly told
> When the winds is bleak and the nights is cold;
> No such life can be led on the shore
> As is had on the rocks by the ocean's roar.

BILL LUCAS AND ANDREW SPEDDING

Yottigation

(From *Sod's Law of the Sea*)

Sod's Law – that if anything can possibly go wrong it does – works at sea just as much as it does on land. Rather better in fact. So when Bill Lucas and Andrew Spedding produced a book on the subject, appropriately called Sod's Law of the Sea, *it found an immediate niche on my bookshelf as funny books are always worth having, and funny books about the sea are only slightly less rare than hen's teeth. I've chosen their piece which gives a few tips on how to play at one-upmanship while navigating. It's essential reading!*

Dear David

This is an important subject and requires a lengthy letter.

Yottigation is an art – Navigation is a science. Owing to the violent motion, inability of yacht helmsmen to steer a course, and likelihood of large compass errors when the boat is heeled or has a kedge anchor parked alongside the binnacle, the science of coastal navigation is theoretically easy to learn but impossible to practice in a small boat. What is needed is the experience and art form of the Yottigator.

Sadly, no one will ever be grateful to a Yottigator. If he brings the boat spot on the button to a buoy the far side of the Channel he will not be praised – the crew will quietly talk of the 'Jammy so-and-so' and congratulate each other on the good course they steered with the marginal adjustments they introduced to 'help him' during the two night watches. If the crew steered a wild course trying to hold a shy spinnaker all night and wandered between south and west in a poor attempt to steer 215° W, not finding the buoy will be entirely his fault.

Yottigators can only overcome this natural adversity by two gambits which introduce elements of doubt about the ability of the crew to steer a good course, the reliability of the compass, the amount of leeway the boat makes, etc., long before anyone is blaming anybody for a bad landfall. This is best done by having a slide rule and suddenly darting up to the cockpit, giving the helmsman a penetrating look and telling him he has been making good 240° for the last hour and what does he think he's steering (actually he's making a passably good job of steering 230°). The other trick is to sight across the compass and look at a setting sun or low star and come back after a flick through *Reed's Almanac* to announce that the port compass is reading 3° high, the starboard compass 4° low – please take note, helmsman. Reverse this and in the logbook write '1816 Sun Azimuth port compass 3° low, starboard compass 4° high'. You can then produce the written evidence in your defence whilst floundering round the Cherbourg peninsula wondering if you can see Cap de la Hague or Barfleur.

If you are the navigator of a frigate, when you have checked the gyro compass to nil and ordered the coxswain to steer 235°, the incidence of him going in some other direction is low owing to a long naval tradition and the Queen's Regulations and Admiralty Instructions. In a yacht the factors which achieve that direction are far more uncertain:

235° on the compass may point to some other direction owing to a recently introduced and unknown deviation;

The helmsman may settle his myopic line of sight with a large angle of parallax on the compass card;

The spotty youth on the wheel thinks he knows that 220° would be a far more hopeful course to get to Alderney;

A sailing boat tending to come up into the wind will attract a helmsman above his course, and he will be pleased to think he is steering a good course by pulling the boat down to the right direction every five minutes or so.

Invariably four of these will apply at the same time in a sailing boat, and three in a motor boat.

Yottigation requires that you think of some arbitrary course in the general direction you wish to travel, and set the lads off to make the worst of that, and whilst feigning some other yottigation chore check with your handbearing compass the direction they actually achieve. You can then make adjustments to suit the various combinations of helmsman, personal feelings, failing eyesight and so on. Getting a boat organized down the same track as your theoretical pencil mark on your chart is the first, greatest, and by far the most important factor of the true Yottigator.

If you achieve this and apply some of the simple rudiments of common navigation you will start to achieve a reputation as a wizard navigator, on the strength of finding France when and where you predicted. You can then start hamming it up a bit to generate a sort of mystique about the whole operation.

This is helped if you make some really lucky navigational breaks, like arriving in thick fog off the Morlaix River and then saying 'I think we are coming into Roscoff harbour' and without seeing the outer breakwater arrive in the inner harbour (don't try this unless you're fairly sure it is Roscoff). A particularly lucky break one summer when we were feeling our foggy way back from Brixham by Braille was to sail over the shallow patch a few miles east of the Eddystone. A non-Yottigator would have run up on deck and leaped up and down shouting 'I've found us' or something silly. A real Yottigator keeps this gem to himself, alters course to allow for the tide and just clear the western breakwater of Plymouth, and then wanders up on deck and starts rolling a set of dice. On the fifth roll you change course 5° and on the seventh role change back 5° the other way. You then pick up the dice, put them back into the leather wallet, and as you go down the companionway tell the congregation that they will see the western arm of Plymouth breakwater on the starboard bow in about four and a half minutes. If at that stage you have been floundering about in the fog for sixteen hours no one will ever again challenge your expertise.

The danger is of nosy non-Yottigators trying to snoop at your charts and check your information. Don't make it easy for them: write as much irrelevant information on the chart as possible, leave your previous voyages unerased amidst a wealth of coffee stains and slightly plastic soaked paper so that they can see little of the printed word. If they ask, place your whole hand palm down, fingers outstretched on a chart of the English Channel and Western Approaches and say, 'We're about there, Cecil.'

They will persistently ask how long it is before you get there. A difficult question this. If you have a couple of birds aboard who are dying of seasickness the honest reply of 'about fifteen hours more' will be enough for them to reach for a handbag and take an overdose of Valium. Equally, a precise answer will not be easy if you have a very sketchy idea where you might be . . . hedge your bets. To the seasick always tell them another three-quarters of an hour. To the nosy crew make it complicated: 'Well, Cecil, if we keep going like this I suppose we might just take the tide off Alderney and make it by midnight, but it's too early to tell yet, Cecil. We'll have to wait and see if we can get the lift or not. Also depends on if you lot are making a decent course, ha ha, and we'll probably lose the wind west of the Casquettes.'

If you work out the tides that have affected your progress to date, and make good the course you intend, and keep a record of how far you travel, you will be as good a navigator as goes. The majority of apprentice Yottigators don't get those first essentials right, and then start getting frenetic with pieces of equipment to further confuse the issue.

The biggest confuser of Yottigators (unqualified) is one of the many forms of radio direction finder. Unbelievably, very few Yottigators ever try to take RDF bearings to test their accuracy when *they know where they are*. they wait to get the headphones out and start trying a bearing of Start Point when they feel they are probably somewhere in mid-Channel. Big ships with stable platforms, calibrated loop aerials and trained operators get absolutely rotten results from DF bearings. Yotties taking bearings alongside the engine block with a boat leaping about get even worse ones. Amazingly, however, because the set was expensive a greatly unfounded faith is applied to it, and having established a sort of null between 340° and 030° the Yotti gets his blackest pencil and draws a thick line down the 005° direction. He then does the same from the St Catherine's Point and Roche Douvre beacons. This gives him a cocked-hat triangle about the size of the county of Rutland and he estimates roughly where Oakham is, jams down a dot, puts a ring round it and pencils in the time.

It has very little to do with where he is . . . but he feels better about it.

Far more accurate guides to general position are the headings of a number of merchant ships travelling in the same direction indicating the shipping lanes they are, or are meant to be, in; regular air flights, and cross-Channel steamers. An even better one is to hoist the two-letter code signal Church Pennant over Interrogative, indicating to the informed passer-by 'God, where are we?' Or call up a merchant ship to ask for a position – if the ship answers in Panamanian, Greek or Taiwan Chinese tell them where *they* are.

In thick fog avoid asking people swimming or fishing off the beach for directions. Take the fact you can see them as an indication of shoal water: asking them if they know where the Clipper buoy or Ramsgate harbour is will merely elicit that they are strangers to those parts.

Yottigators need very little equipment but what they do need requires careful preparation. Their pencil, eraser and dividers will all attract unlikely uses for other people aboard, and should therefore be tethered on lengths of string like the café teaspoon. Dice, one set numbered, one set liar already mentioned, a set of charts suitably overwritten and a *Pilot* book or two, an old copy of *Reed's* with a modern set of tide tables, and an AA book and railway timetable to add to the mystique. One item which is needed and also needs preservation is a pair of binoculars: these should be adjusted to your eyesight and then heavily boat taped in the right focus. Tell your friends this is to keep the water out. Actually it's to stop them using them when you most need them.

As a final wrinkle to Yottigators: don't be fooled into thinking that what you actually see is the bit you expect (and want) to see. Check and doubt yourself.

One of those old flying boats came down in the China Sea when we were puffing our way up to Shanghai once. We were asked to look for some recently marinized RAF types and set off in the general direction. As we got into the search area a speck was seen on the horizon. The pulse of the ship went faster and more and more goofers came up to the bridge, all with shiny binoculars acquired in Aden and little used since. The chief steward started the rot: 'I can see a tailplane.' The chief engineer then saw the engines, the radio operator saw the RAF markings, the watch-keepers were getting a bit edgy about the whole thing because all they could see was a speck and were beginning to feel they would fail their next Board of Trade eyesight test. The second steward saw some men standing on the wing, and the purser someone waving a white towel. At about eight miles we were being treated by the gallery to descriptions of handlebar moustaches and wings on their tunics, and at four miles an apprentice unwisely stated that it looked more like a Korean fishing boat to him. At three and a half miles it clearly was a fishing boat, and at two miles it was a Korean one.

In the way of an unfair life the apprentice got absolute hell from everyone for weeks, but it only goes to show how easy it is to delude yourself into seeing what you expect to see. If you expect to see Barfleur lighthouse, make darned sure it is that before getting cocky about your landfall.

Chay Blythe and Robin Knox-Johnston plus eight million Australians can tell you of the funny light effects you can get where the Antarctic draft meets the hot Aussie airs of Wilson Promontory. This can sometimes cause the land to look upside down (confirming what many think about Australia anyway), and sometimes for images to split, two ships steaming at you, one the right way up and one sailing along on its funnel. All good stuff for curing alcoholics and amusing passengers after long voyages. What is very unusual is another ship coming at you down a line of mixed hot and cold air which splits the image. One big passenger ship sighted exactly that, two images

'Sorry, mate – I'm a stranger here myself'

alongside each other right ahead. The navigator broadcast this interesting fact to the passengers who downed their drinks in a panic to run and see the most interesting outboard event since the Suez Canal. One liberty ship came down the port side, and the second one, steaming parallel to it, down the starboard.

With the exception of the master, most observers were very impressed.

Two white lights and a green one above may look like a fishing trawler to you, and from where you think you are this makes good sense. The experienced Yottigator toys with the idea that this could also be a frontal view of Broadstairs High Street.

Yours, etc.

JOHN SCOTT HUGHES

'Twice Round, Sir?'

(From *Little Ships*)

One treasures that story of the diminutive yacht (in the
Channel Race of, I think, 1928) which reached the finishing line
after two long days and two even longer nights of wet, windward
driving. As the finishing gun was fired the drenched and weary
but indomitable paid hand turned to his owner and, in all good
faith, shouted, 'Twice round, sir?'

WILLIAM TRAVIS

Fortune Bank and Ishmael

(From *Shark for Sale*)

I read Shark for Sale *in the early sixties when planning the route home for* Suhaili *from Bombay. It is a fascinating account of the author's attempts to set up a commercial shark fishing venture in the Seychelles using a local boat and crew, and I drew a line straight to the Fortune Bank, the scene of this small extract. Unfortunately, I never got there as I ran out of monsoon time and had to head straight down the coast to Mozambique. Perhaps it's just as well, as we all need places to dream of visiting.*

For the next two days we sailed on southwards, across the invisible *bordage* and out into the realm of the great ocean itself, for on this voyage our destination was a distant *sec* known as Fortune Bank. My reason for choosing this area was its very remoteness, for I knew the fishing schooners seldom if ever visited it, not daring to leave the main Mahé plateau and sail out over the deep water that separates the two banks. Here I hoped to find sharks in profusion, roaming freely over the shallows during the day as they had once done around Mahé. A quick and successful trip now would go a long way toward providing the new gear needed to continue with the night drift-line experiment.

The morning of the third day found me patently anxious as to whether we would find Fortune Bank, for a high overcast hid the sun and made my sextant, on which we relied to ascertain our position, completely useless. As the morning advanced,

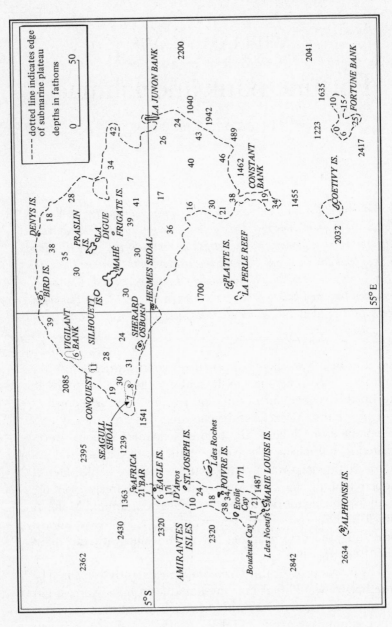

Seychelles Group (Northern portion only)

however, so did Ton Milot become more and more cheerful, until at length I was forced to ask him the reason.

'Of course I'm happy,' he said. 'We're nearly there! Another hour or two and we'll see sharks enough to fill the boat. How do I know? Easy. Look at that,' he pointed over the side. 'See that strip of seaweed? That's from La Fortune, that is. Look how green it is. It's been floating for less than twelve hours otherwise it would be brown all round the edges. That means we must be within six or eight miles of the *sec*. Another thing. See the way it lies in the water? It's taken up the lie of the current and we're sailing parallel with it, so La Fortune must be dead ahead. Ton Milot doesn't need a sextant and a pile of complicated books to tell him where he is. He just sniffs the air, cocks an eye at the sea and if he's still none the wiser the seagulls take pity on him and whisper in his ear. *Ou capable croire!*'

Less than an hour later the old man beckoned me forward to where he was lying in the shade of the jib. Without saying a word he pointed ahead. At first I could not see anything, then on the horizon, a faint cloud of minute specks became visible. They were seabirds following a run of fish, and birds in these numbers, far from land, meant fish in considerable quantities. Moreover, such shoals were usually only to be found along the edges of the banks. Sure enough, as we drew nearer the demarcation of a *bordage* became visible: a slow coiling ribbon of disturbed water whose inner edge was marked by eddies and wavelets.

Such easily visible signs of the presence of a *sec* beneath the surface are to be found only where the drop-off into the abyss is unusually abrupt, causing violent up-wellings along its front. Even then these tell-tale signs are often lost to view in the general movement of the sea's surface, unless the day is unusually calm, as it was then. This time we were fortunate in having both of these factors in our favour, the location of the bank was made easy for us.

An atmosphere of unrest and of anticipation crept over our little ship. We were expecting great things from Fortune Bank and the three-day voyage across the lonely sea had served

merely to whet our appetites. Now we were nearly there and the
waiting was almost over. Without any of the usual promptings
on my part the others had laid out their lines and were making
the *Golden Bells* ready for the work that lay ahead. Up in the
bows Ishmael was hard at work on a lance head, honing it to a
bright, razor sharpness. Astern, Gandhi had let go two of our
heaviest shark lines, baited with strips of a small tunny caught
earlier that morning. These streamed behind us, ready for any
cruising shark that might cut across our wake. Ton Milot
doused the deck planks with a last bucket of sea water to ensure
that no foot would slip.

There was nothing else to do. We were ready and the ripple
marked edge of Fortune Bank was now less than 200 yards
away.

'Aiee-yah! *Guette ça!*' It was Hassan at the helm, and before
we were able to turn around we felt the deck tilt under our feet
as he jammed the rudder hard over. The others, by long experience, knew instinctively what had occurred and immediately
swung into action. Ti-Royale cut the throttle and put the motor
out of gear, and Ton Milot ran down the jib and foresail in a
welter of canvas while Gandhi paid out on the mainsail boom.
In a few moments the cutter was brought to a near standstill,
lying across the breeze. By this manoeuvre the two lines that
had been hanging limply astern were brought into the beam,
but one of them was no longer hanging limp. It was stretched
bowstring-taut, dangerously near breaking point. Even as I
watched, the other line twitched suddenly and pulled rapidly
downwards, drawing off the slack that lay coiled on deck until
it, too, was brought up with a jolt by the ringbolt to which it was
fastened. Hassan, already trying his hardest to release some of
the tension from the first line, was powerless to deal with this
second strike. The swarthy Zulu was first to his aid but he, in
turn, only served as another human spring, taking the edge off
each fresh, savage jerk that threatened to snap the line. After a
few moments Gandhi and Ti-Royale arrived and there were
two men to each line. Then Ishmael, Ton Milot and myself.
Seven of us, and it seemed as though we were trying to drag up

the ocean bed itself. A fathom or two would come in and then we would be brought to a halt. The line would grow heavier in our grasp, stretching visibly, and we would be forced to give way, losing perhaps all we had gained. Another heave: another small gain, and so it went on. Our breathing became laboured. Sweat ran slippery down our backs and into our eyes, causing them to smart and sting. But the line was coming in.

Slowly, almost imperceptibly, the downward pull of the two sharks grew weaker. First one man was able to drop out and then another, until there were three of us free to prepare the wire nooses, lances and lifting gear. Leaning far out over the side to see how near the surface the fish were, I discovered that the two lines had become tangled and the sharks, both large Peau Claires (Greater White Tipped), now lay side by side, securely trussed and snapping ineffectively. Such a situation could be dangerous, since both beasts would now have to be dealt with at the same time.

Once on the surface the wire nooses were quickly slipped over their snouts, but so completely had these sharks tangled themselves up in the lines in their struggles that very little of their heads remained to be seen, being swathed in coil upon coil of shark line. To drive the lance in without cutting this and thus freeing the creatures would take the utmost skill. After a short discussion this harpooning was entrusted to Ishmael as being the ablest and most experienced harpooner on board. Under his instructions we brought one shark right alongside, immediately below the spot on deck where the gaunt spearman chose to stand. Ti-Royale handed him his weapon, that same one which he had spent so much time and care in bringing to the exact degree of sharpness. He hefted it in his hand, feeling for the point of balance. Satisfied, he glanced at us ranged on either side of him and with a jerk of his head indicated that we were to stand well clear. With feet braced wide apart and left arm extended palm downward for balance, he raised his other arm – the one holding the lance – until he was one straight line from toe to harpoon butt. At the last moment he baulked, unsure of his stroke. Several times he did this, but Ishmael was taking no risks. He knew his work and the rest of us were silent.

At last he struck, his body curling like a released spring as his whole weight followed behind his arm movement. The lance head bit deep into the beast, burying itself completely within the carcass. As the stroke ended so Ishmael's body began to uncoil again in a swift, sinuous motion designed to pluck the lance from the shark's vitals. But the huge creature came to sudden and unexpected life, writhed grotesquely and tore the haft from the fisherman's clutching fingers. For a second he staggered, thrown off balance by the unexpected jerk. Then his right arm shot out as he sought to regain it.

Meanwhile, driven by pain, the shark lashed itself furiously against the side of the boat and the haft of the lance beat the air wildly above the level of the bulwark. Ishmael, oblivious of the danger, thrust out his arm in the direct path of this gigantic metronome.

There was a dry report, like a brittle stick snapping, and his arm was broken just below the elbow. Before the shock had registered, the return stroke caught him on the wrist, smashing this too, the force of the blow swinging Ishmael around to face us.

He stood there woodenly, jaw agape, his right arm held before him like a lop-sided 'Z'. The shark gave a last desperate wriggle; the embedded lance head sliced neatly through the line and then the shark was gone in a tremendous swirl of water. In the moment of stillness that followed my eyes remained fixed on a splintered white end of bone that had broken through the Creole's brown skin and now stuck up in the air at an oblique angle.

'*Ou capable croire?*' whispered Ton Milot, and this time the familiar words seemed like a prayer. I raised my eyes to Ishmael's face in time to see the greyness flood into it and great drops of sweat burst out on his forehead.

'What shall I do?' he moaned softly, flapping the useless appendage in front of him as if to shake it off.

'Christ! What a bloody mess!' said Ton Milot in a natural tone, and turned away.

The others had gathered in a little group and were whispering among themselves. I pulled myself together and bade Ishmael follow me down into the cabin. Once there I sat him on a box of fishing tackle and took a look at his arm. As Milot had said, it was a mess. Both ends of the radius were pulverized, with jagged splinters of bone slicing through the flesh at various points. Several small bones in the wrist appeared to be smashed as well. While I was examining it I was conscious that there was neither morphine nor splints in the small first aid kit with which I had equipped the boat.

I motioned Ishmael to lie down on Ton Milot's old mattress and then broke up the wooden crate on which he had been sitting. I yelled for Gandhi, as being the strongest, but without result. Sticking my head up through the hatch I saw that the rest of the crew had succeeded in geting the other shark on board and were busy catching more. Gandhi seemed to resent my interrupting his fishing and grumbled as he followed me down into the cabin. Telling him to hold Ishmael tightly under the armpits, I took hold of the mangled forearm and straightened it as much as possible without causing him undue pain. Then, with no indication of my intentions, I transferred my grip to his hand and pulled on the limb with all the strength I could muster. For a second Ishmael's green cat's eyes opened wide in startled horror, then they glazed over and the yell that was on his lips died in a gurgle as he slumped forward in a dead faint.

His arm was still far from straight but the ugly splinters of bone were no longer exposed to view, nor the nerves left raw to the air. Using the pieces of crate, padded with cotton wool and sail canvas, we managed to fix a reasonable splint, which we lashed in place with fishing line. The whole process was completed before Ishmael recovered consciousness. Leaving Gandhi to prepare some tea for him, I went on deck to speak to Ton Milot.

'All right, Ton Milot,' I said. 'Let's finish off now. Get the lines in and we'll set course for Mahé.'

'Sweet Mother of God! You mean we're going back?'

'Of course. We've got to get Ishmael to hospital.'

'Hmm. Look, m'sieur. Your business is your business, this is your ship and we're your crew, but Sweet-Jesus-and-All-the-Angels, we can't leave now! Not with all these sharks about. Not because a bloody fool Creole busts his arm. We can't do it! We've got to stay, begging your pardon. Even if Ishmael's arm drops off we can't go back now. These sharks are money to us and a profit to you. We can't go! To hell with the bastard!'

The rest of the crew, hearing their coxswain's outburst, joined in as well: 'But no. We can't go back . . .'

'. . . first time we've hit sharks like this in ten years'.

'. . . not leave La Fortune. Not now . . .'

'. . . *tant pis*, Ishmael . . .'

They were sullen, vociferous and scared. Scared of having to leave, of not returning to Fortune Bank, of losing the few rupees the sharks meant to them.

In the wake of the silence that followed Ishmael could be heard moaning down in the cabin. 'Aiee-yi-yi. Aiee-yi-yi. Aiee-yi-yi . . .,' over and over again as the pain set in.

Zulu and Hassan looked momentarily startled, then their faces clouded over with sullenness again. The rest pretended not to hear, but nevertheless looked uncomfortable. They waited for me to reply, but I held my tongue for a while in order to let Ishmael's keening sink in. Then I explained that we must go back, and we had no option. But I promised them we would return to La Fortune as soon as possible.

They turned away without saying any more, but by the way they set about their work it was apparent that they resented my decision deeply. Moreover, they did not believe we would ever come back again. For them Fortune Bank was not named after Kerguelen's brave little ship, but because a 'fortune' of sharks lay there. It had always been a near myth to them, a shark fishermen's Elysian Fields. Now we were going back and the illusion they had held for a brief while was shattered.

A little later I went down to see Ishmael. He was still crooning to himself: 'Aiee-yi-yi. Aiee-yi-yi,' over and over again. In my brief absence his condition had worsened considerably. He was running a fever, his eyes were sunken, his head rolled from side to side and his whole body was bathed in sweat. I dosed him with Codeine tablets, gave him a shot of penicillin, loosened the splint bindings for a minute or two and left Gandhi to keep an eye on him. When I went back on deck Ton Milot was alone at the helm, the others having disappeared into the fo'c'sle.

For several minutes we sat in unfriendly silence till the old man raised a scrawny arm and pointed out abeam. At first I could not make out what he had seen. Then an indistinct bubble of whiteness appeared for a moment, only to vanish again over the horizon. Five minutes later it reappeared, and thereafter at more frequent intervals, until by the end of half an hour it had resolved itself into a large full-rigged ship. This vessel was heading in the same direction as we were, but on a slightly converging course, that brought her gradually nearer. Presently she was close enough for us to be able to identify her as one of the rare trading schooners that ply between Mauritius and Mahé, 1200 miles of deserted ocean, the loneliest trade route in the world.

When the two ships were a mile or so apart I took the tiller from Ton Milot and pointed up at our sails. There was no need to say a word; he had the same idea in mind when he first pointed the vessel out to me. He grinned his old, foxy grin and went forward, pausing only to yell down into the cabin: 'Hey, you. Ishmael! You bloody fool! You're going to sleep in a nice bunk tonight and tomorrow night you'll have a nice little nurse to keep you company and hold your hand. *Ou capable croire!*'

These were the first words spoken to the gaunt fisherman by the other Creole since his accident.

In the next few minutes I brought the *Golden Bells* hard across the newcomer's path and hove to. That the other ship had seen us and was aware of our intention was obvious when she was yet a mile away, for we could see her sails beginning to shake and flutter as the halyards were slackened prior to taking them in.

'What do you want?' yelled a figure from the cabin roof as soon as the large vessel was alongside. 'Food, fuel or a course for Mahé?'

'None of those.' I shouted back. 'Can you take an injured man on to Mahé for us? You're faster than we are and he needs the attention of a doctor badly.'

'Surely,' came the reply. 'What's the trouble?'

While I was explaining, Gandhi and Hassan brought Ishmael up from out of the cabin and between them passed him over the bulwark onto the other ship. As they did so I caught a brief glimpse of the injured man's face. It was fantastic how it had altered in the past hour. Ishmael had always been gaunt, but now he was like a spectre; the flesh had fallen from his cheekbones and his eyes were dull coals in cavernous sockets.

In a matter of minutes the transfer was completed. Ishmael was somewhere below in a decent bunk, the master had been fully informed of the cause of the accident and held in his hand my explanatory letter to the hospital authorities. Neither vessel wished to prolong the rendezvous. The others were eager to get under way towards Mahé and my crew were equally anxious to be off in the opposite direction, back to Fortune Bank. As we cast off and the gap between the two ships widened, none of the Creole fishermen on board the *Golden Bells* bothered to look back. For them the episode was finished, even as was Ishmael's future as a fisherman, which they all knew. *Tant pis*, Ishmael....

Due to adverse currents it was mid-afternoon before we struck Fortune Bank again; this time we did not stop at the *bordage*, but sailed on over that area of ripple-marked water until we were well onto the shallows, where the dark blobs of coral outcrops showed clearly on the seabed, eight fathoms down. Here we anchored and, after cooking and eating a meal, the first that day, went to bed with the setting sun.

Dawn found us motoring southwards to establish ourselves on the furthest tip of the bank and there to follow its contours back northwards, fishing as we went. During that day and the four that followed we both saw and caught more shark than ever before or since. Fortune Bank, unfished for years, surpassed even its legends. Each time we looked over the side, it was to see the sinuous, wallowing shapes of at least half a dozen great beasts cruising near at hand. In five days we took on board a dead weight of eighteen tons and lost three times that amount due to snapped lines, mishandling and the rolling overboard of various carcasses that were piled three or four deep upon the deck in a way that threatened at times to capsize us.

At first we began by piling all the sharks head downwards in the sunken cockpit. Thus their deadly jaws were safely out of the way should they momentarily revive, for we had no time to ensure that each and every one was really dead before giving our attention to the next. We soon found, however, that even this procedure was not safe, for in the final death flurry their great tails, raised high above deck level, would thresh wildly, striking down or overboard anyone within range. The first to be struck was Ti-Royale, who received a cuff across the side of the head that sent him right over the stern, almost on top of a large hammerhead that had been drawn alongside prior to lancing! In his desperation to get back on board, the young Creole swung a foot onto the shark's back and, by pushing hard downwards, succeeded in getting himself up out of the water. He was able to grab the rudder stock and was back on deck again within a matter of seconds.

The next victim was myself. This was a comparatively gentle love tap that caught me across the shoulders, knocked me down, neatly skinned a large portion of one shoulder-blade and left me with a bruise that lasted for several weeks.

Finally, Milot nearly came to grief but ducked just in time and, except for getting his hat knocked off, managed to escape. After this indignity he took upon himself the task of lopping off the tail of each and every shark as soon as it was safely on board. There was only one drawback to this procedure: in the final convulsion gouts of thick blood would spout from the severed ends of the trunks, covering us all with its congealing redness. After a few futile attempts to escape these 'blood baths', we ignored the heavy spurts which drenched us at each death. The blood never had a chance to dry upon our skins, for we were continually showered with fresh drops. But even if we could not keep ourselves clean, we learned that the decks must at all costs remain spotless. If we allowed a puddle of blood to lie undisturbed on the wooden planks, it would thicken and become as slippery as a layer of heavy oil. Such a hazard could send us sprawling headlong, perhaps within snapping distance of a freshly caught and very lively shark that had that moment been brought on board.

Each day we worked without a thought for food, rest or cleanliness. With the coming of dusk we coiled our lines, dropped the anchor and sought out a place to sleep among the high-piled carcasses. Ton Milot showed me how to make a comfortable and secure bed under such conditions. Two large sharks beneath one as a mattress, two more on either side as bolsters to prevent one from rolling overboard and another across the top on which to rest one's head. The hide of a shark does not hold water, nor is it slimy. Their bodies made a firm yet resilient support, not unlike that of an air mattress. Thus cradled by the bodies of our daytime catch we slept securely.

RICHARD MAURY

The Forgotten Steamship

(From 'Curious Records of the Sea')

In the Merchant Marine humorous reference is often made to a mythical steamer (sometimes known as the Tuscaloosa City) having sixteen smokestacks, an equal number of decks and a straw bottom. Actual history reveals a forgotten steamship no less fantastic. In the 1850s one Darius Davison of New York designed and built, of iron, I believe, the steamship *Leviathan*, a mammoth cigar-shaped craft with an inverted bow. Seven hundred feet in length, she was designed to carry 3000 passengers across the Atlantic at a speed of 30 knots. This vessel had not sixteen smokestacks but thirty-two all told, and sixteen engines. She never made 30 knots, for on her trial trip with every engine wide open and her funnels belching out a furious smoke screen, she barely touched 4. She sailed no more, and was soon forgotten.

BROOKE HECKSTALL-SMITH

The *Sybarita* and *Kariad* Match of 1901

(From *All Hands to the Mainsheet*)

I've chosen this description of a classic yacht race which took place long ago because it's as exciting a piece of sporting journalism as I've read anywhere. It comes from a book called All Hands to the Mainsheet *by Brooke Heckstall-Smith who was a very well known sailing journalist during the great Edwardian yachting era and after. The two yachts he's writing about here, the* Sybarita *and the* Kariad, *belonged to that elite class which included Lipton's* Shamrocks, *the German Emperor's* Meteor, *and the* Britannia. *They were quite enormous by today's standards and must have been a magnificent sight. The match Heckstall-Smith describes took place in the Firth of Clyde, which I know well as I live on it. The race was round Ailsa Craig – or Paddy's Milestone as it is sometimes called as it is halfway between Scotland and Ireland – a great rock at the entrance to the Firth and which, on a clear day, I can see from my bedroom window. It was a rough day when the race took place; the yachts were very evenly matched. Mile after mile, for seventy-five miles, they raced neck and neck with the huge crews fighting to keep the enormous yachts under control. It must have been an unforgettable day and Heckstall-Smith, who was on board the* Sybarita, *describes it all with marvellous clarity.*

One night, nearly twenty years ago, I was on board a big racing yacht called the *Sybarita*. She was lying at her anchor in the still bay at Rothesay – 8 June 1901 – a beautiful evening. We had been racing there and had sat on deck late after dinner, Percy

Thellusson, du Boulay and myself, watching the fading glories of a summer's day over that lovely anchorage. We had seen the last of the red sunset glint upon the tall golden spars of the racing fleet. *Shamrock I*, the Kaiser's great Scottish yawl *Meteor*, *Kariad*, a grand first-class cutter, *Lais*, *Carina*, *Nevada* and Mr Connell's *Tutty* were all around us. We had seen the mountains of Loch Striven, wondrous in the half light that casts mysterious shadows and soft colours upon their heathered slopes, and we had gone below, for the hour was late, though daylight still lingered in those high latitudes.

I was sitting in the broad saloon yarning with du Boulay beneath the cabin lamp. Thellusson a few moments before had bid us turn it out and go to bed, and he himself had gone to his cabin. It was extraordinarily still, as it is in these sheltered, tideless anchorages of the Clyde when the night is calm. We could not even hear the crew snoring in the forecastle, as no doubt they were, tired after racing, but the *Sybarita* was a big vessel, 213 tons.

There were noises on deck as of a boat coming alongside, and Thellusson reappeared in the doorway to tell us we had visitors – crowds of 'em; they were on deck now and coming below. What was the nature of their call at this hour, nearly midnight, he did not know. We rang for the steward for glasses, soda water, replenished decanters – that trusted servant had not turned in. We were instantly prepared for any invasion. They should not tell us 'this ship was longer between drinks than she was between perpendiculars'. That would never do, after all the hospitality that had been shown us on the Clyde!

Our guests were soon seated. I do not remember how many of them there were, but eight or ten, and some of the younger ones seemed pretty merry and bright. The nature of their visit was soon explained. What was the fastest yacht afloat? That was the question. They had been discussing it at dinner, and the matter was still in dispute.

I must now explain that in this year it had been arranged that all the fastest great yachts in Europe should sail two races on the Clyde, on 7 and 8 June 1901. These yachts were two cutters

89

belonging to Sir Thomas Lipton, *Shamrock I* and *Shamrock II*, Mr Kenneth Clark's cutter *Kariad,* the German Emperor's yawl *Meteor* and the *Sybarita,* of which my old friend, Percy Thellusson of Ryde, was in command. These were the great racing yachts of 1901.

Sir Thomas Lipton's *Shamrock II* had a short time before been dismasted in a trial off Cowes, when King Edward VII was on board, and although no one was hurt in this accident, *Shamrock II* was not rerigged and fitted out in time to take part in these races.

The races had been sailed at Rothesay on 7 and 8 June, with the following results:

First Day, 7 June

	H	M	S
Sybarita, winner	7	14	34
Meteor	7	42	56
Kariad	7	47	2
Shamrock I	7	47	36

Second Day, 8 June

	H	M	S
Shamrock I	6	32	7
Kariad, winner	6	34	47
Sybarita	7	10	33
Meteor	7	12	20

The dimensions of the yachts were:

	Rig	LWL	Beam	Sail area	Rating
Shamrock I	cutter	90	24.7	14,215	113.4
Sybarita	yawl	90.6	23.0	12,072	103.4
Kariad	cutter	86	20.0	10,505	94.1

The German Emperor's *Meteor* was about the same size as *Sybarita.*

So when our visitors came on board on the evening of 8 June the great races were over. The issue, however, 'What was the fastest yacht afloat?' was still unsettled. At least they said so. They said the matter could only be settled in one way – namely, by a fair and square race on YRA time and rule. It could not be decided by argument or by all the square roots and calculations in the world. We in *Sybarita* had won the first race; *Kariad* had won the second race. Winds had been light and each had had a turn of luck. That had nothing to do with it. Every yachtsman knows such things happen in every yacht race. Lipton was out of it; his yacht *Shamrock I* had been beaten. Kaiser William was out of it; his yacht had been beaten. The issue, therefore, rested between *Sybarita* and *Kariad*. Each, so far, had won one race, and Mr Kenneth Clark contended that his cutter *Kariad* was really the best, but his friend, Mr James Coats, on the other hand, believed that *Sybarita* was the best. They told us they had talked the matter out, but both were agreed that there was only one way to settle it – the old-fashioned way, *sail a match* – sail a match to settle the question what was the fastest vessel on this side of the Atlantic.

We all agreed that the question could not be decided in any other way. The idea appealed to me immensely. I listened with keen attention. What about *Shamrock II?* She doesn't count; she has been wrecked and has not got a mast, a very necessary detail in any yacht race.

Mr Thellusson said that he could not claim that *Sybarita* was the faster, for although he had won yesterday, he had been beaten today by the *Kariad*. Perhaps there was a sporting offer in the wind. The hour was late, but the subject was interesting and the situation was unique. The company was the best and the whisky was John Jameson.

There was a sporting offer in the wind, and this is what it was. Mr James Coats explained it. He owned the big schooner *Gleniffer*, now lying in the bay. She was not a racer; if she were he would race either *Sybarita* or *Kariad*. He had owned many racers in bygone years. The *Marjorie* was his best. He owned no racer now. But if Mr Thellusson would sail he would bet upon the *Sybarita* for any sum, great or small, to beat the *Kariad*. If the *Sybarita* won, his friend Mr Clark, the owner of *Kariad*, would pay the owner of *Sybarita* the stakes. If *Kariad* won, he, Mr James Coats, would pay Mr Clark the stakes.

Mr Kenneth Clark accepted the offer, provided, of course, Mr Thellusson would allow the *Sybarita* to sail. It would be really good sport and decide the issue, if Thellusson did not object. Mr Thellusson agreed he would sail.

The amount of the bet was agreed by Mr Clark and Mr Coats as a mere matter of detail. 'Five hundred pounds,' the owner of *Kariad* suggested. 'Guineas,' said Mr Coats, and the point was settled.

'But, my dear James,' said George Watson, who was the designer of both yachts, 'you'll understand this is the most extraordinary bet so far as you are concerned. If *Kariad* wins you stand to lose five hundred guineas; but you don't stand to win anything, because if *Sybarita* wins the money has got to be paid to her owner.'

'I understand it very well, George,' replied that great old sportsman. 'That is precisely my intention. The money makes no difference to me, all I wish for is – a race.'

We decided to sail the match at 10.30 o'clock on Monday morning, 10 June. What about the course? I suggested we should sail round Ailsa Craig and back.

'That is a mark that will not shift,' dryly remarked Mr Coats, and the matter ended.

So our visitors got into their boat and rowed away, bidding us 'goodnight' and 'good luck'.

We sat round the table in our cabin pondering over this strange visit. What yachtsmen! What sportsmen they were! They had but one object in view. *Sybarita* and *Kariad* they considered were the best boats in the fleet; which was the faster they did not know. Let a match be sailed to decide. 'Monday, 10.30 a.m., YRA Rules and Time Allowance, Ailsa Craig and back, 75 miles, 500 guineas.' No quibble about conditions or argument about detail. It was a sporting match if ever there were one.

It was, of course, decided that Mr James Coats, the backer of *Sybarita*, should sail with us. He was then an elderly man and frail, but as keen as ever.

On Monday we put to sea for the race, but before the start a slight accident to *Kariad's* bowsprit bitts caused her to be unable to sail, so the race was postponed until Tuesday, 11 June.

The fresh breeze of the previous day had hardened to nearly a full gale of wind, and the news of the match had, of course, spread like wildfire amongst all the sportsmen and old salts on the Clyde. Folks assembled on Bogany Point wondering what was going to happen, but the general opinion ashore was that modern racing yachts would not venture to face the broad expanse of open water off the Mull of Cantyre in such weather, nor would they take the risk of a catastrophe to spars and gear in the wild seas that must be running by the Ailsa Craig. When crews began getting top-masts down it was soon realized that the yachts meant business, and by 10 a.m. both left their moorings with double-reefed mainsails and small jibs and with their topmasts housed. The *Sybarita* was carrying a small triangular mizzen.

With the full force of the north-westerly gale on the starboard beam, the yachts started for their match at 10.30 a.m. We crossed the line about a length ahead of the *Kariad*. Captain Bevis was steering the *Sybarita,* and in those days a 90-footer was steered with an enormously long steel tiller instead of a wheel, such as is now used in all large vessels. The yachts set their foresails as the starting gun fired. *Kariad* thus had double-reefed mainsail, working foresail and a small jib; we in *Sybarita* the same, with the addition of the little triangular mizzen. I do not know if this small mast and sail on the end of our tail was doing any good, but it seemed to be pulling its weight. We tried to set a mizzen staysail, but before it was half tacked the mizzenmast bent like a whip and I thought the whole lot would go over the side, but we scrambled down the mizzen staysail just in time to save it and shoved it in the sail locker. The *Kariad*, in the foaming track of our wash, gradually fell about a dozen lengths astern. The next move was that they shifted the working foresail on *Kariad* for the balloon staysail. Racing fashion, of course, we followed suit. Our balloon foresail was a big, light-weather sail and in the gale it would not stand at all, and down it had to

93

come, and we reset the working foresail. *Kariad's* balloon foresail, however, was a better sail and was drawing grandly, and
during the reach past Mountstuart to the Cumbraes, in fairly
smooth water, it enabled her to hold onto us well. Abreast of
Garroch Head both yachts had as much wind as they could
stagger under, and I estimated they were travelling about 14
knots. *Sybarita* was now leading by about a minute and a half
and the vessels were making good weather of it. We kept well to
leeward of Lamlash, and the heights of Holy Isle were given a
wide berth for fear of getting a lull off the land, for we were
determined to drive the *Sybarita* today. The *Kariad* was steered
in our track and was sailing practically the same speed as we
were. Gradually we both brought the Pladda Lights and
Kildonan Point abeam and were pounding heavily into the full
weight of the gale, no shelter now to windward between the
yachts and the Mull of Cantyre. Eleven miles of angry white
crests before we could reach the Ailsa Craig. I shall never forget
it: the great sea and the glorious manner the *Sybarita's* great
pram bows charged at it. She was a light displacement vessel
with hollow section, and drew 17 feet of water. She went flying
over the crests of the waves like a porpoise at play, over one sea
and smashing down into the next, throwing showers of white
spray over herself from stem to stern, clean over the top of the
mizzen. One can hardly credit it.

Steam yachts which had followed us on our passage, including Sir Thomas Lipton's steam yacht *Erin*, now put back to the
more sheltered waters of the inner Firth of Clyde; they could not
face the fury of the storm. Old Mr James Coats, who had bet
upon the *Sybarita,* had arrived on board two hours before the
start. He was an eccentric old gentleman, and having the best
cabin placed at his disposal by Mr Thellusson, promptly retired
to bed. He said he did not wish to be disturbed. He brought two
personal servants with him, who gave us this message when he
retired to rest. We had started, with all the roar and racket of
racing going on above deck. The work of setting and handling
canvas, which, with a crew of thirty-three hands all shouting
and hauling, makes a deuce of a noise, had proceeded, but

apparently Mr Coats was undisturbed. We had not seen him for the first twenty miles of the race. Now, eleven miles off the Ailsa Craig, amidst the flying scud, his kind old face appeared in the main hatchway.

I went to him. Would he have some refreshment? No, he would take nothing. He took nothing to eat nor drink the whole day. He looked at his rival the *Kariad*; she was not far astern – two minutes or less. 'How much do we give her?' he asked. 'Eight minutes,' I told him. 'We shall win,' he said. I doubted it then, but told him we meant to do our best and the ship was going well. 'Sail her hard! Sail her hard! Drive her!' said the frail old gentleman, rubbing his thin white hands. 'Drive her! Drive her!' he repeated, half to himself. 'She will stand it. Two reefs down, two reefs; better with one, better with one. Drive her!' said the old man.

He was right. The great *Sybarita* was a ship which could be driven; but we had two reefs in the mainsail and, with the wind now two points before the beam and a mountainous sea roaring through the lee scuppers, this could not be altered.

'I wish to speak to the mate,' he said. I called the mate aft, and Mr Coats bade him tell the men be careful lest no man go overboard in the great sea. He said in days gone by he had, on such a day, lost a man from his yacht *Marjorie* and he wished them to be careful now.

All this time, and indeed throughout the rest of the race, he sat in his shirtsleeves and would wave aside anyone who suggested he should wear coat or oilskin.

As we approached the Craig the great rock – our mark – 1100 feet high, loomed up in the mist. The wind and sea had remained two points before the beam since we opened Pladda. *Kariad* had then been obliged to shift her balloon foresail, but Mr Kenneth Clark did not do so until his yacht had got the utmost advantage out of the sail. Neither before nor since have I seen a balloon foresail stand like it. Why the sail was not blown to ribbons is a mystery. Generally such a sail is a poor thing in a hard breeze, but *Kariad's* was a good 'un.

The Craig was before us. In the squalls the sea was surging

through our lee rigging like a millrace, and the *Kariad* hidden from our view by storms of cold rain and hail. Onward we thrust into the long crested rollers. The Craig at last!

We are under its lee, to leave it to starboard; right under its lee now like a white snow fleck beneath its huge black height. Into a sudden lull we come suddenly onto a level keel and take an alarming list to windward. 'Hold on, men on the weather deck!' 'All hands on the mainsheet!' shouts Bevis. 'Now's your chance to get it in!' Onto the mainsheet we tailed, head sheets also, and trimmed her down to closehaul out to windward of the rock and tack round it. We were soon clear of the big lull. One or two little ones, then hard puffs, and we were threshing to windward in the most tremendous sea to fetch out to a safe point to put helm down and tack, to leave the Ailsa Craig to leeward. Close hauled and threshing dead into it, the spindrift was perfectly blinding. We being leading boat, *Kariad* could watch us, and of course profit by any bad luck we might have in the lulls under the Craig, and she did so by steering a little wider of it and cleverly avoiding the worst of them.

Watching for a slightly smooth patch in the wild expanse of broken water, for it was a nasty job to tack, our helm was put down and round we came. 'Ease the mainsheet! Keep charge of it. Keep another turn on!' I heard du Boulay's order, but some hand had not kept guard over it and had not sufficient turns on, and the soaked white rope was slithering out over the gun-metal cleat till it steamed with the friction and the main boom ran off nearly to the rigging!

It was jammed at last, but it was a nasty position, dashing along, wind on the port quarter and the Ailsa Craig close under our lee; so close – only a few yards; and I could hear the shrieking of the thousand gannets and seabirds as they rose, disturbed by the flying *Sybarita*. Onto the main sheet we got again, a mighty haul of sailormen, thirty-three hands on the mainsheet, all a-hauling of her like Trojans. It was a tremendously heavy job to get her trimmed just right for a quartering wind before the gale. Glad we were, and breathless too, when Bevis said: 'Belay try that!' as the old phrase runs.

But we were homeward bound now and had got round the Craig in the heaviest sea that ever was known in a sailing match.

	H	M	S
Sybarita	1	40	0
Kariad	1	43	45

Those were the times we tacked as I roughly took them, but whether we had tacked in the same water to get round so bold a mark as the Ailsa Craig, who can say?

We may have lost as the mainsheet ran out. I know, when I looked at the *Kariad* a little while later, I estimated that she could not be more than 2 minutes 30 seconds astern. Eight minutes we had to give the smaller vessel; gallantly had she sailed. How could we do it? More than half the course was gone already.

With the wind and sea a point or two abaft the beam, it was a very different job going home. The worst of the heavy pounding had ceased, and the farther we drew into the Firth of Clyde the more we eased the seas and smoothed the water; but the roaring gale was as hard as ever. We dropped our opponent a little; off Pladda she was about 3 minutes 40 seconds astern, and by holding too much on our weather quarter and standing in too close to Holy Isle she lost another minute and a half.

It was now a desperate race for *Sybarita*, because we had only about twenty miles more to run and still, so far as I could judge, about three minutes to wipe off. We set the balloon foresail, but it gave us no advantage, because *Kariad* set her balloon foresail at the same moment.

The *Kariad* had just passed Holy Isle when a blinding storm of hail and rain came sweeping down from the mountains and she was lost to view in the mist.

Could we shake out a reef without the *Kariad* observing it? If she saw us doing it she would follow suit and the labour would be lost, because the relative speeds of the yachts would surely be unchanged. To shake out a reef without being seen was our one chance of victory. The sea was smoother, and Captain Bevis, with Captain Mountefield assisting him at the tiller, was keeping the big ship very steady. Off the Isle of Arran a hand went out along the main boom of the *Sybarita*. The main boom was well off over the sea on the starboard side and heaving a good deal. It was a galvanized steel tube of great diameter. The sail was laced to it and the reefing in one or two long lacings, not in 'reef points', for such were abolished in racing yachts before that date. The hand – I can see him now, a little chap as active as a monkey – had a clasp knife in his hand and as he went out along the boom he cut the lacing as he went.

Beginning at the tack in this way, the strain of the wind in the sail forms a good belly before the boom, and the man crept along in the bunt of the sail hacking the lacing in front of him until he got to the clew and then cut the earing. It was a smart piece of work. Now every man got on the main and peak purchases and, after a strong pull, the sail was raised, with the yacht driving upon her course.

The *Kariad* had not seen that we had shaken out the reef. Now with only a single reef in the mainsail, instead of two, the *Sybarita*, with the fair wind and the smoother water inside the Cumbraes, was off like a hare.

I have been told by those along the shore that the sight of the *Sybarita* passing Mountstuart on 11 June was most wonderful to see.

In those days gear was strong. The mast, a fine Oregon spar, you could give the vessel the entire weight of the gale of wind in a yacht like the *Sybarita*, and on an occasion like this probably the mast of one of the *Shamrocks* would have gone overboard. Just as the *Sybarita* went tearing past Mountstuart the sun came out through the clouds, and looking back I saw that the vessel was leaving a smoking track of spindrift for nearly a hundred yards astern and the sun was casting miniature rainbows upon its whirling flight. I could see also that we had beaten the *Kariad*, for since we shook out the reef she had rapidly grown smaller and was now nearly two miles astern. It was wonderful. We were doing 14 knots, but she was more than eight minutes behind us, and in every mile we were adding to our lead. Bogany Point was in sight. It was plain sailing. We sat on the saloon floor and had a drink! The angle of heel was pretty great. 'The five hundred's all right,' I said. 'Looks like it, if nothing carries away,' Thellusson answered, but he had no sooner spoken than there was a crack like a pistol shot. 'What's that?' we both exclaimed, preparing to rush on deck. 'Rivet head sheered off in one of the stringer plates, I expect,' replied du Boulay, who is a good engineer and generally right; and this is probably what it was, for the strain was tremendous and on deck they had heard nothing.

Gun! a puff of smoke and the match was over.

	H	M	S
Sybarita, winner	4	40	0
Kariad	4	50	43

We had sailed seventy-six miles, with the distance of tacking round Ailsa Craig, in 6 hours 10 minutes.

Such is the story of the Ailsa Craig Match, and I think it remains still, after many years, one of the most memorable races in the history of the Clyde.

Mr James Coats had scarcely spoken all day, and we could not, at any time, persuade him to either eat or drink. Now it was over he said little, but his kind old face was flushed with pleasure.

'You understand, you *quite* understand, we are the greatest friends,' he remarked, and for the moment I did not know to whom he was referring, until he continued: 'But for that reason I wished to beat him. I *wished to beat him*. The sport was in me, but I had no yacht of my own. If Watson or Fife could have built me one in a day I would have ordered one – if it cost a fortune – to beat him. It is kind of you all; it is kind of Mr Thellusson and of the crew; they are *men*. I thank them all. A great race! Kenneth is beaten! We are great friends, you *quite* understand,' he added. Then he left in his long, six-oared boat, which came to fetch him from the *Gleniffer,* his schooner. But before he went he handed the steward a roll of notes, £50, to give to the crew – 'For their kindness,' he said. So this strange old gentleman, leaning upon a thick stick, for he was lame and an invalid, went upon his way happy.

It was the last race sailed by James Coats.

Note: In this match the copper sheathing on the *Sybarita's* bows was stripped off on either side for a length of twenty feet abaft the stem; this was caused by pounding into the heavy seas at high speed.

ALFRED, LORD TENNYSON

The *Revenge*

(A Ballad of the Fleet)

I

At Flores in the Azores Sir Richard Grenville lay,
And a pinnace, like a flutter'd bird, came flying from far
away:
'Spanish ships of war at sea! we have sighted fifty-three!'
Then sware Lord Thomas Howard: ''Fore God I am no
coward;
But I cannot meet them here, for my ships are out of gear,
And the half my men are sick. I must fly, but follow quick.
We are six ships of the line; can we fight with fifty-three?'

II

Then spake Sir Richard Grenville: 'I know you are no
coward;
You fly them for a moment to fight with them again.
But I've ninety men and more that are lying sick ashore.
I should count myself the coward if I left them, my Lord
Howard,
To these Inquisition dogs and the devildoms of Spain.'

III

So Lord Howard past away with five ships of war that day,
Till he melted like a cloud in the silent summer heaven;
But Sir Richard bore in hand all his sick men from the land

Very carefully and slow,
Men of Bideford in Devon,
And we laid them on the ballast down below;
For we brought them all aboard,
And they blest him in their pain, that they were not left to
    Spain,
To the thumbscrew and the stake, for the glory of the
    Lord.

IV

He had only a hundred seamen to work the ship and to
    fight,
And he sailed away from Flores till the Spaniard came in
    sight,
With his huge sea-castles heaving upon the weather bow.
'Shall we fight or shall we fly?
Good Sir Richard, tell us now,
For to fight is but to die!
There'll be little of us left by the time this sun be set.'
And Sir Richard said again: 'We be all good English men.
Let us bang these dogs of Seville, the children of the devil,
For I never turn'd my back upon Don or devil yet.'

V

Sir Richard spoke and he laugh'd, and we roar'd a
    hurrah, and so
The little *Revenge* ran on sheer into the heart of the foe,
With her hundred fighters on deck, and her ninety sick
    below;
For half of their fleet to the right and half to the left were
    seen,
And the little *Revenge* ran on thro' the long sea-lane
    between.

VI

Thousands of their soldiers look'd down from their decks
    and laugh'd,

Thousands of their seamen made mock at the mad little
    craft
Running on and on, till delay'd
By their mountain-like *San Philip* that, of fifteen hundred
    tons,
And up-shadowing high above us with her yawning tiers
    of guns,
Took the breath from our sails, and we stay'd.

VII

And while now the great *San Philip* hung above us like a
    cloud
Whence the thunderbolt will fall
Long and loud,
Four galleons drew away
From the Spanish fleet that day,
And two upon the larboard and two upon the starboard
    lay,
And the battle-thunder broke from them all.

VIII

But anon the great *San Philip*, she bethought herself and
    went
Having that within her womb that had left her ill content;
And the rest they came aboard us, and they fought us
    hand to hand,
For a dozen times they came with their pikes and
    musqueteers,
And a dozen times we shook 'em off as a dog that shakes
    his ears
When he leaps from the water to the land.

IX

And the sun went down, and the stars came out far over
    the summer sea,
But never a moment ceased the fight of the one and the
    fifty-three.

Ship after ship, the whole night long, their high-built
    galleons came,
Ship after ship, the whole night long, with her battle-
    thunder and flame;
Ship after ship, the whole night long, drew back with her
    dead and her shame.
For some were sunk and many were shatter'd, and so
    could fight us no more –
God of battles, was ever a battle like this in the world
    before?

X

For he said 'Fight on! fight on!'
Tho' his vessel was all but a wreck;
And it chanced that, when half of the short summer night
    was gone,
With a grisly wound to be drest he had left the deck,
But a bullet struck him that was dressing it suddenly dead,
And himself he was wounded again in the side and the
    head,
And he said 'Fight on! fight on!'

XI

And the night went down, and the sun smiled out far over
    the summer sea,
And the Spanish fleet with broken sides lay round us all in
    a ring;
But they dared not touch us again, for they fear'd that we
    still could sting,
So they watch'd what the end would be.
And we had not fought them in vain,
But in perilous plight were we,
Seeing forty of our poor hundred were slain,
And half of the rest of us maim'd for life
In the crash of the cannonades and the desperate strife;
And the sick men down in the hold were most of them stark
    and cold,

104

And the pikes were all broken or bent, and the powder was
    all of it spent;
And the masts and the rigging were lying over the side;
But Sir Richard cried in his English pride,
'We have fought such a fight for a day and a night
As may never be fought again!
We have won great glory, my men!
And a day less or more
At sea or ashore,
We die – does it matter when?
Sink me the ship, Master Gunner – sink her, split her in
    twain!
Fall into the hands of God, not into the hands of Spain!'

XII

And the gunner said 'Ay, ay,' but the seamen made reply:
'We have children, we have wives,
And the Lord hath spared our lives.
We will make the Spaniard promise, if we yield, to let us go;
We shall live to fight again and to strike another blow.'
And the lion there lay dying, and they yielded to the foe.

XIII

And the stately Spanish men to their flagship bore him
    then,
Where they laid him by the mast, old Sir Richard caught at
    last,
And they praised him to his face with their courtly foreign
    grace;
But he rose upon their decks, and he cried:
'I have fought for Queen and Faith like a valiant man and
    true;
I have only done my duty as a man is bound to do:
With a joyful spirit I Sir Richard Grenville die!'
And he fell upon their decks, and he died.

XIV

And they stared at the dead that had been so valiant and
    true,
And had holden the power and glory of Spain so cheap
That he dared her with one little ship and his English few;
Was he devil or man? He was devil for aught they knew,
But they sank his body with honour down into the deep,
And they mann'd the *Revenge* with a swarthier alien crew,
And away she sail'd with her loss and long'd for her own;
When a wind from the lands they had ruin'd awoke from
    sleep,
And the water began to heave and the weather to moan,
And or ever that evening ended a great gale blew,
And a wave like the wave that is raised by an earthquake
    grew,
Till it smote on their hulls and their sails and their masts
    and their flags,
And the whole sea plunged and fell on the shot-shatter'd
    navy of Spain,
And the little *Revenge* herself went down by the island crags
To be lost evermore in the main.

HAMMOND INNES

Business in Deep Waters

(From *Punch*)

Hammond Innes, of course, is not only a prolific thriller writer – one of the top names in the game – but a very experienced yachtsman. So it's not surprising that quite a few of his novels are sea based, as it were. And highly readable they are too. But instead of taking an extract from one of them I've chosen instead an amusing and perceptive piece he wrote for Punch *some years ago about the charter business. I've done some chartering myself and know how far from the truth are the dreams of so many people of earning a living from their love and knowledge of sailing and doing it under a tropical sun with the tiller in one hand and a rum punch in the other. The facts are very different! But for the customer, as Hammond Innes reveals here, to charter a boat can be a marvellous experience.*

The footloose traveller in denims stood on the Long Pier beside me, both of us waiting for the government launch to disgorge our baggage, and I asked him where he was going. 'India,' he said.

'Flying?'

'No, yacht.'

'You work in India?'

He shied slightly at the word. 'No-o. Boat's bound for Singapore. From there I'll pick up something going on to Perth – maybe then I'll get a job.' He said it without conviction, a sop to the conventional way of life.

These are the new-style remittance men, who live tax free

and rent free from one yacht to another on what their fathers toss their way. Girls, too, a world of footloose youngsters who drop in and drop out of any place with an anchorage, passing the time and vaguely looking for something they will probably never find.

Anyone who (for the experience, or to get to some out-of-the-way bird island) uses the services of the yacht charters will almost certainly come across them. The world of professional sailing is now a very odd one. Not unattractive. Just not concerned with the world we live in, only in making ends meet in the way of life to which they have become addicted.

And for the youngsters who drop out in this strange fashion it's not at all a bed of roses.

Alas, they are but human. On the quays and in the bars you see them getting older. They get married, just like other people, grow up into skippers – then what was fun becomes a business. And it's hard on the girls they marry. . . .

'I was cooking for ten – breakfast, lunch, dinner. That's sixty plates to wash up. They were Germans, mountains of food, then an Italian film unit, twenty-four hours to turn round, all the victualling.'

Some of the skippers are also owners, men who have put what capital they had into the '£200 millionaire' dream, sailed halfway round the world to find inflation catching up with them and have turned to chartering because time has passed them by and they are not qualified to earn their living in any other way – don't want to, anyway. Touting for charters in tourist hotels and on the waterfront, they have to accept what comes, a constant invasion of their beloved boat, strangers without references, who may be alcoholics, cardiac cases, potential suicides or just plain boors.

The most expensive charter boats are often owned by real millionaires. I lay alongside one such boat in Corfu, a huge new schooner immaculate from a Genoese yard. It was owned by an American businessman and when I asked the skipper why he bothered with charters, he said, 'Oh, it's not the owner. It's the crew.' He was an ocean racing man and he had just had a cracking sail, not caring overmuch that the charter party had been cabin-confined with seasickness. 'You can't keep a team as keen as this rotting in harbour ten months of the year.'

Later I saw him much further south in the little port of Gayo. He was rushing about in the yacht's speedboat, while the charter party sedately explored the village and its excellent fish restaurant. We saw him a year later in the Aegean, tramping past at 12 knots, and I envied him a little, doing pretty much what I was, but being paid for it.

And his clients – weren't they getting what they wanted, too? I went into it at the time. With accommodation for twelve on board, it worked out at slightly less per head than a luxury hotel. And luxury hotels don't take you to the remotest islands of the Aegean!

A few weeks ago, on the island of La Digue on the Indian Ocean, two of us were able to charter a well-known ocean racer for the day. We sailed to the little out-island of Grande Soeur – twin granitic peaks and in the flat land between a single planter's house built of takamaka wood. We shared our lunch with that lonely Seychellois family, using the wellhead for a table, and left laden with new-picked limes after having walked a hundred yards through the palms to the far side where the swell rolled in onto the blinding glare of a coral sand beach. Two hours later we anchored off the edge of the reef by Albatross Island, a fortress pile of rock surmounted by a few palms, went into a sheltered sandy gut in the inflatable and swam for hours as the sun went down in a kaleidoscope of piscine colour. Not in the Maldives, a thousand miles to the west, nor even on the Great Barrier reef, have I seen such a variety of fish and water of such marvellous clarity.

All around the world now yachts provide a service, giving travellers the opportunity to explore islands and coasts and reefs not served by any other means. No matter that you feel obliged to entertain the skipper ashore, or that in places like the Mediterranean he may have his own pet restaurant where, you suspect, he gets a rake-off. No matter that drinks on board are extra and the 'friends' who crew for him are often thirsty folk.

It is still a world apart, the best means bar none, of getting away from it all.

How else could you possibly experience a day such as I have described in the Indian Ocean; the cost, believe it or not, was less than £9 each. And should you think, when you have fixed a charter, that perhaps you are being taken for a ride, do your sums and work out what it would set you back to have a boat of your own waiting for you with skipper and crew, ready victualled, to go to Aldabra or the Galapagos, or simply on a fortnight's cruise in Greek waters.

But don't treat a yacht as a luxury hotel. Do it for the adventure. And remember occasionally that, though you are paying, for the people who sail you it is their home. And if you think the Aegean, which is so accessible, will be full of tourists, I can only say that in three seasons in my own boat we hardly saw a soul, wandering an island world little changed since the days of Odysseus. There is no cruising ground anywhere quite so fascinating.

ANTHONY HECKSTALL-SMITH

The High-Hat Club

(From *Sacred Cowes*)

The American bewilderment concerning the Squadron was summed up for me one day by Lucy Briggs-Cunningham, whose husband was a member of the American team. We were standing together on the lawn, when she began asking me the names of the owners of some of the yachts lying in the roads.

'Who owns that one over there with the black and white ports and the fancy rig?' she asked, indicating the *Fanthom*.

'Ernest Guinness,' I told her.

'What, the guy that makes the Guinness?' she questioned.

'The same,' I answered.

'And that cute little black steam yacht?'

'That belongs to Richard Hennessy.'

'Hennessy's brandy?'

'The same family.'

'What about the big white ketch?'

'That's *Cariad*. She belongs to John Gretton. He makes the beer called Bass,' I added, unable to resist the temptation.

'But they're all flying the White Ensign, and that means they're all members of the Royal Yacht Squadron?' my companion asked incredulously.

'Correct – perfectly correct. You're learning fast Lucy,' I encouraged.

'But I just don't understand. You say all those guys make hooch and yet they're members of this club?' A note of astonishment stressed the question and I remembered that this young American was a product of the Prohibition Age.

'Yes, they're all members,' I assured her.

'No kiddin'! And they told me this was a high-hat club!' she laughed.

BILL TILMAN

Heard Island and Port Aux Français

(From *Mostly Mischief*)

Bill Tilman, the author of Mostly Mischief *from which this piece is taken, became a legend in his lifetime in two sports, mountaineering and sailing. He seemed to take a delight in going to sea in boats that others considered unseaworthy, and he always headed for unfrequented parts in order to climb inaccessible peaks. His favourite type of boat was the old Bristol pilot cutter, the first of which was* Mischief. *He wasn't a single-hander, always taking a crew. He sometimes had trouble with them as he was quite unconcerned with comfort and had a passion for curries, which he ate continuously. In this extract he is down in the Southern Ocean, cruising around as if it were the English Channel. This was some years before Chichester, Rose and I were 'pathfinding' our way through those incredible seas! Apart from my natural admiration for a born adventurer and first-class seaman, my other reason for reading his books is that forty years later I grew up at his old school, Berkhamstead. Perhaps it is the bitterly cold winds that blow through the Tring gap in the Chilterns that educated us for the Roaring Forties!*

Bill Tilman disappeared with his boat and crew somewhere in the South Atlantic in 1977. One cannot help feeling that it was the way he would have wished to go.

The strong north-west wind that presently got up enabled us next evening to round Cape Digby at the north-east corner of the island. There, on the lee side of the island, we had smooth water and ran fast all night down the east coast. By daylight

Kerguelen was out of sight. The cold now became more appreciable, the sea temperature 39° F and the air 43°, for we had now crossed what is called the antarctic convergence where there is an upwelling of cold water. At 8 a.m. of the 7th, fine, sunny, and windy, we were some ninety miles from Heard Island and early that afternoon, when we were still sixty miles away, we sighted Big Ben. There was no mistaking the characteristic lenticular cloud sitting over the summit and below it the glint of white snow slopes. That evening we sailed close by the McDonald Islands, three barren rocks, steep-to all round. No one has yet landed on them and it was in our minds to make an attempt. For this we needed a calm sea and the sea at this time was far from calm. The islands are some thirty miles west of Heard Island and in a freshening wind we ran towards it at 5 knots until midnight when we hove to about ten miles short of Winston Lagoon.

In 1962 the ANARE ship on its way to Mawson, the Australian Antarctic base, had landed on Heard Island a party of four which included Warwick Deacock and Grahame Budd. In the course of an attempt on Big Ben, after putting a camp at 4000 feet, they had been driven down by snow and gales. The route they had then taken, starting from Winston Lagoon, had appeared most promising, and on this account Winston Lagoon or its vicinity had been chosen as the place to put the present party ashore. Moreover, we entertained a faint hope that we might take *Patanela* into the lagoon itself where not only could a landing be easily made but where *Patanela* might safely remain while the party were on the mountain. There was no sheltered anchorage elsewhere. Even at Atlas Cove at the north-west end of the island where the Australians had their base, one would need to be in constant readiness to clear out at short notice.

By next morning the wind had died and except that the glass was falling conditions for a landing seemed fair. When we anchored in five fathoms about a quarter-mile off the lagoon the wind showed signs of stirring but fortunately from offshore. We had envisaged sending a raft into the lagoon to take soundings but we had not to worry long about that. Even with the slight swell then running the water broke white right across the entrance, and seaward of the shingle spit that almost enclosed the lagoon huge boulders showed above the water. Both rafts were inflated and launched, one to be used as a stand-by rescue launch, and the loads got on deck. The breaking water on the bar discouraged any idea of taking even a raft in but west of the lagoon was a small beach where we could see some sea elephants and a penguin rookery. From the beach access could easily be had to the ridge called the South Barrier and so on to the mountain.

At that moment a raft might have got ashore but in order to establish the shore party for a month two trips would have to be made and the unloading and reloading would take some time. Before committing ourselves we waited a bit for the weather to declare its intentions. We did not have to wait long. The wind quickly rose to gale force. The strain on the cable proved too much for the electric winch so we got the anchor by hand and let the boat drift off shore. The wind had settled at north-west and when about a mile out we got the parachute anchor overboard in the hope of stopping or lessening the inevitable easterly drift. All along we had been at great pains to get to windward of the island and to stay there, to avoid at all costs having to beat back to recover it. The anchor held us almost stationary for nearly an hour until under the combined weight of wind and boat it gave way. The fitting between the anchor chain and the nylon parachute cords parted and although we re-rigged it with more shackles we finally had to haul it in and resign ourselves to drifting eastwards.

Hove to on the port tack we drifted to the south-east for the best part of two days until the wind moderated enough for us to begin motoring. A sight at noon of the 11th put us fifteen miles nearer the island than I expected, our total drift having been only about forty miles. Soon we sighted the island and at the same time the wind increased again to nearly gale force. But we had the island in sight and this time we were determined not to let go of it. We plugged on until we had gained the lee of the east side of the island and by evening were anchored off the

115

Compton Glacier. Except that it afforded shelter from any wind between north-west and south-west the anchorage had few charms. True we could see the snow slopes and ridges of the mountain, but shorewards, instead of a beach, we beheld merely black ice cliffs about 100 feet high. The Compton Glacier extends into the sea and owing to the amount of debris it carries the ice is more black than white. To the south of us, where is Spit Bay, we could make out the seas breaking on the low gravel spit which extends seawards to the east for five miles.

This spit which protects Spit Bay and the east coast of the island from southerly winds lay between us and Winston Lagoon. To round it and reach the lagoon we had about twenty-five miles to go and in order to be there in good time we started soon after 3 a.m. on the 12th. Owing to the swell left by the recent strong winds the sea breaking on the bar across the lagoon looked worse than it had three days before. We anchored off the small beach while Warwick, who had to make the decision, gazed long and earnestly at the surf. The decision made, no time was lost in loading the raft and at 11 a.m. it started for the beach with the five men of the shore party, Colin driving. In case of mishap Russ stood by with the Zodiac raft which by now was less seaworthy than one would wish. The rest of us watched their progress with anxiety as the heavily laden craft vanished in the trough and reappeared on the top of the swell. Soon we saw them stop outside the breakers to await their opportunity. What happened in the few, critical moments among the breakers we were too far off to see but we were heartily glad when we next saw the raft being hauled up the beach.

Nearly an hour then elapsed before we were in contact with the shore party and learned how they had fared, both ship and shore party being provided with walkie-talkie sets. All had gone well until the raft capsized in shallow water at the edge of the beach with three of the party underneath it and the Johnson outboard still running. The load had been well secured so that nothing was lost but a camera, and since the party were wearing wet suits they remained more or less warm in spite of their ducking. Warwick added that the surf was then too bad to launch off for the second trip. We agreed to wait until evening in the hope that it might go down.

We saw them put the tents up high above the beach and then early in the afternoon we heard that they were about to launch. This they achieved and Warwick with Colin came off for the second load of stores. All went well on the second trip and by 4 p.m. the shore party were safely established with a month's food and we had squared up on board and were ready to go. February 11th was the day appointed for our return. I wanted to pass round the west side of the island, a part we had not yet seen. But off Cape Lambeth only a mile to the west, the tents of the shore party still in view, we met a strong breeze while ahead of us stretched a long line of white water. No reef or spit lay in that direction, the water was being lashed by sudden and violent wind. We stood to the south to make an offing, handed the sails, and lay to under bare poles.

By next morning we were able to set the foresail and start sailing assisted by the engine. After a night of drifting we were not likely to fetch the west of the island and in due course the east coast showed up wide on our port bow. At noon, in bright sunshine we had Spit Point abeam. For the moment we were in calm water and in spite of being short-handed we hoisted all the sails hoping that the shore party would take note of this defiant gesture. A freshening wind soon made her too hard to hold. When the island disappeared that evening in a bank of fog we were once more under short canvas. Gales, sunshine, rain, and fog – we had had them all in the inside of a week. Happily, the vexed seas round Heard Island are free from ice and icebergs.

With a crew of five we had only one man on watch. Tony Hill, Russ Pardoe, Malcolm Hay, and I did two-hour watches, while Ed Reid who had the wireless to look after did the cooking. We missed Warwick. Ed positively liked food out of tins but he soon learned to his dismay that his favourite, baked beans, was on the proscribed list. Ed's wireless transmissions, or attempted transmissions, took up a lot of time. We were a long way from anywhere, certainly too far from Australia to make contact. The

117

news that the party had landed on Heard Island went by way of Mawson in the Antarctic. Some of his messages went by way of Cape Town and one by Singapore.

With Kerguelen lying 300 miles to the north-west, that is to windward, I expected a hard passage. In fact, with moderate winds, and those generally from west or south of west, we had no trouble. On the evening of the third day we sighted Presqu'île Monarch at the south-east end of the island and next day we were motoring against a strong head wind up the broad Baie de Morbihan. This bay has many ramifications and Port aux Français, the French base, lies up in its north-eastern corner in what is probably the most exposed part. The bay is big enough to provide a long 'fetch' so that in a hard gale there may be waves two to three feet high outside Port aux Français. Its saving grace is a patch of kelp across the entrance, thus the small piece of water inside remains pretty smooth even in a gale. Since *Mischief's* visit in 1960 three mooring buoys for three landing craft have been laid. There is therefore not much room left for anchoring and none at all for dragging.

We had timed our arrival to a nicety. When the Chef de Mission came on board to welcome us he announced that lunch was on the table. Jeeps took us the few hundred yards from the little concrete jetty to the common messroom where the odd hundred men and one woman who then comprised the base were already seated. Amidst a great welcoming uproar of cheers and banging on the table we took our seats. We had an undeniably excellent meal, a meal such as only Frenchmen could produce on what is a desert island if you exclude innumerable rabbits and the quarter million sea elephants and a million penguins that inhabit the flat beaches of the east coast. I noticed my companions going at it hammer and tongs, Malcolm having a slight edge on the others, but to me it lacked the relish and refinement of our first meal here in 1960 when M. Perrimond presided over the cuisine. Or perhaps then, after the spartan fare of *Mischief*, I was in a more appreciative mood than now after weeks of high living in *Patanela*.

As coffee was being served the whole assembly began chanting a refrain, 'Cognac, Odot, Cognac, Odot, Cognac!' I grasped the significance when after about five minutes of chanting M. Odot rose to his feet and produced his keys and presently the brandy began to circulate. He was the quartermaster, intendant, or steward, a short, stout man with an imperial, far more respectably dressed than anyone else. The chanting then began again: 'Cigar, Odot, cigar, Odot, cigar!' and once more M. Odot complied, and cigars were handed round. Perhaps the presence of guests made him more amenable. Once more the chanting broke out: 'Merci beaucoup, merci beaucoup, merci!'

After lunch we made a tour of the base, visiting the various huts where extremely intricate machines were ticking away day and night recording upon reams of paper whatever they were recording – obscure phenomena from the ionosphere or maybe the stratosphere. Their earnest, bearded attendants explained to me what each was doing. After the lunch we had had I was not in a receptive mood. My French being little and my knowledge of science less, I felt that they might as well have addressed their remarks to the moulting king penguin that I had observed standing forlorn and disconsolate by the flagstaff outside the messroom. Aided by the woman scientist who spoke some English I found the launching site for hydrogen balloons slightly more intelligible. While on our way in we had remarked the huge screen erected for protecting the balloons while being inflated and had mistaken it for a block of flats. In connection with the balloons, a mast seventy metres high was in process of erection, a considerable feat of engineering in view of the rocky ground and the force of the winds it had to withstand.

I was surprised at how few of the French, several of them very learned men, spoke any English, far more surprising than the fact that only one of us far-from-learned men spoke any French. Russ and Malcolm could sometimes be heard uttering what they thought might be French, but Tony who had spent a year studying in Paris spoke it pretty fluently and acted as interpreter. The base had expanded considerably since 1960 when the personnel numbered only seventy against 120, though we were told that in winter only about thirty are left there. And besides the new base at Christmas Harbour, a base had been established on Ile de la Possession in the Crozet group at Baie du Navire, the anchorage where we had spent a fortnight in *Mischief*. I was told that a *téléferique* now passed directly over the king penguin rookery through which we had so often fought our way – a piece of news that decided me to write off Baie du Navire as a place to be revisited.

Another change that had taken place was the closing down of the plant for extracting oil from sea elephants – they had, of course, first been slaughtered. This had been run by a private company which had permission to kill up to 2000 annually. The late manager of this, a tall, fair Frenchman speaking excellent English, known as the Viscount (and I believe he was a Viscount) was marooned at Port aux Français with neither instructions, money, nor even a passage home. We had thoughts of taking him to Australia but before we left we heard that a passage for him had been arranged.

We had arrived on a Saturday when they had their weekly film show. Before attending we went back on board to change our anchor. The Breton boatswain in charge of all the craft, a man who answered my ideas of a real Frenchman – black hair and moustache, red-faced, stout, with a very loud, hoarse voice – did not think our anchor man enough and loaned us a much heavier, stockless anchor. On this anchor we lay quietly enough till the Monday when I thought it time to move on. We had more than a fortnight to put in before our Heard Island rendezvous and did not wish to trespass for so long on French hospitality. On the Sunday they had insisted on our having all our meals ashore and for our part we had needed little pressing. As no doubt they would have done at home, they devoted Sunday to *la chasse*, most of the garrison setting out heavily armed and returning at dusk either with nothing or perhaps a scrawny rabbit.

With difficulty we persuaded the Chef de Mission and some of the hierarchy to visit us on board for drinks. In the end we mustered quite a crowd. Having given them all their *coup de Scotch* I noticed they were not drinking very heartily and when I took a swig myself I understood why. I had given them whisky and sea water. While they were on board I explained to the Chef de Mission that we would like to spend some time at Port Jeanne d'Arc to which he agreed and at once began organizing things to ensure our enjoying our stay there. From my point of view the chief attraction of Port Jeanne d'Arc lay in the fact that there was a vacant mooring buoy which we could use. Anchoring at Port aux Français was too much like anchoring at a place mentioned in an *Admiralty Pilot*, of which it remarks: 'Anchoring in this bight must be prompted by necessity and not by any hope of tranquillity.'

NEIL HOLLANDER AND HARALD MERTES

Six Methods of Raising a Fouled Anchor

(From *The Yachtsman's Emergency Handbook*)

Overcrowded anchorages must have increased enormously the odds on the weekend yachtsman getting his anchor fouled. He either anchors with everyone else and runs the risk of plaiting his chain with another yacht's or he tries to find a place where no one else will venture – and has a better than even chance of dropping his hook over foul ground. Either way, sorting out the tangle can be a long and tedious business unless you know just how to go about it. Detailed here are six perfectly straightforward methods of tackling what must be one of the most common problems a yachtsman has to face. Failure to get an anchor to bite properly sometimes results in it becoming fouled. To help it bite I would recommend the use of an angel which I first saw used on the west coast of Scotland. It also reduces the amount of yawing whilst at anchor. Once the anchor has been let go and the boat has brought up, a large weight, 50-60 pounds for a 35-footer, is attached to the chain and lowered to the bottom on the end of a line. In calm conditions, the boat will be held by the weight alone, and when it blows up a bit the weight helps to hold the chain close to the bottom and stops the anchor chain being lifted so easily in surges, which is when the dragging usually starts.

METHOD 1

Bring the bow directly over the anchor so that the chain is tight and vertical.

Secure the chain.

Rock the boat, fore to aft, in order to use the boat's buoyancy to break the anchor out.

METHOD 2

Sail or motor over the anchor and attempt to pull it out from the other direction.

METHOD 3

Pass a ring, a large loop, or better still, a bit of chain over the anchor chain and, using a dinghy, tow it down until it reaches the anchor's crown. Then attempt to raise the anchor from the dinghy ■ 31.

METHOD 4

Using a line or chain approximately three times the length of the anchor chain tow the leep as far down the chain as possible. Drop the dinghy's anchor and when it is firmly dug in, then attempt to break the boat's anchor free ■ 32.

METHOD 5

If the anchor is fouled on another boat's chain:

Attempt to raise *both* the anchor and the chain as high as possible.

Pass a line around the chain and secure it to the boat.

Free the anchor by hand or by dropping it

Then release the chain ■ 33.

METHOD 6

If the chain and anchor cannot be raised:

A kedge or dinghy anchor will serve as a grapple.

Once the anchor is hooked, the line can be either pulled from different directions or taken back to the boat where the chain and anchor can be raised with a winch ■ 34.

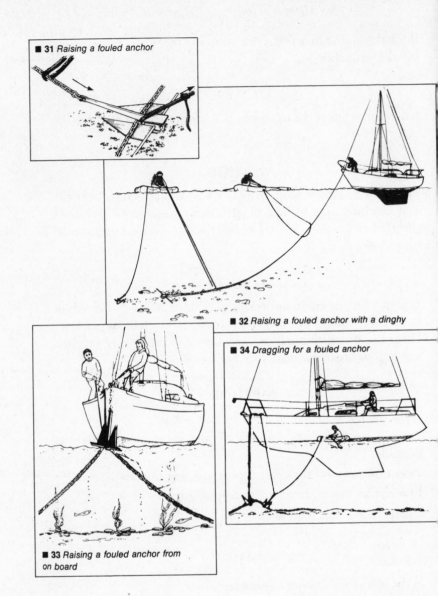

■ **31** *Raising a fouled anchor*

■ **32** *Raising a fouled anchor with a dinghy*

■ **34** *Dragging for a fouled anchor*

■ **33** *Raising a fouled anchor from on board*

C. S. FORESTER

Escape

(From *Flying Colours*)

One of the most fascinating aspects of the Hornblower novels is that C. S. Forester was neither particularly knowledgeable about the sea, nor was he a trained historian. But he went to tremendous lengths to ensure the accuracy of his background, and the many books that cover Hornblower's life give us a vivid picture of life at sea in Napoleonic times. But Forester could not have been a complete landlubber as the idea of the first Hornblower came to him while studying three volumes of the Naval Chronicles *which he had taken aboard a small boat he was about to live on for several months. And Hornblower himself was developed as a character during a six-week voyage back from San Pedro to England in a cargo ship. This extract, taken from* Flying Colours, *the third novel in the series, is part of the chapter describing Hornblower's escape down the Loire from Nantes, and is, I think, a typically exciting piece of Forester narrative. The title of the book, by the way, came from his publisher Michael Joseph, who said, when Forester was explaining that he planned another Hornblower where his hero escapes from the French, 'You want to bring him back with flying colours?' What also interests me is who Forester modelled Hornblower on: Blackwood, Cockrane. . . ?*

Hornblower forced himself to hold up his head and walk with a swagger; the pistols in his side pockets bumped reassuringly against his hips, and his sword tapped against his thigh. Bush walked beside him, his wooden leg thumping with measured stride on the stone quay. A passing group of soldiers saluted the smart uniform, and Hornblower returned the salute non-chalantly, amazed at his new coolness. His heart was beating fast, but ecstatically he knew he was not afraid. It was worth running this risk to experience this feeling of mad bravery.

They stopped and looked at the *Witch of Endor* against the quay. Her decks were not of the dazzling whiteness upon which an English first lieutenant would have insisted, and there was a slovenliness about her standing rigging which was heart-breaking to contemplate. A couple of men were moving lacka-daisically about the deck under the supervision of a third.

'Anchor watch,' muttered Bush. 'Two hands and a master's mate.'

He spoke without moving his lips, like a naughty boy in school, lest some onlooker should read his words and realize that he was not speaking French.

'Everyone else on shore, the lubbers,' went on Bush.

Hornblower stood on the quay, the tiny breeze blowing round his ears, soldiers and sailors and civilians walking by, the bustle of the unloading of the American ships noisy in the distance. Bush's thoughts were following on the heels of his own. Bush was aware of the temptation Hornblower was feel-ing, to steal the *Witch of Endor* and to sail her to England – Bush would never have thought of it himself, but years of service under his captain made him receptive of ideas, however fan-tastic.

Fantastic was the right word. Those big cutters carried a crew of sixty men, and the gear and tackle were planned accord-ingly. Three men – one a cripple – could not even hope to be able to hoist the big mainsail, although it was just possible that the three of them might handle her under sail in the open sea in fair weather. It was that possibility which had given rise to the train of thought, but on the other hand there was all the tricky estuary of the Loire between them and the sea; and the French, Hornblower knew, had removed the buoys and navigation marks for fear of an English raid. Unpiloted they could never hope to find their way through thirty-five miles of shoals with-out going aground, and besides, there were batteries at

Paimbœuf and St Nazaire to prohibit unauthorized entrance and exit. The thing was impossible – it was sheer sentimentality to think of it, he told himself, suddenly self-critical again for a moment.

He turned away and strolled up towards the American ships, and watched with interest the wretched chaingangs staggering along the gangplanks with their loads of grain. The sight of their misery sickened him; so did the bullying sergeants who strutted about in charge of them. Here, if anywhere, he told himself, was to be found the nucleus of that rising against Bonaparte which everyone was expecting. All that was needed was a desperate leader – that would be something worth reporting to the Government when he reached home. Farther down the river yet another ship was coming up to the port, her topsails black against the setting sun, as, with the flood behind her, she held her course close hauled to the faint southerly breeze. She was flying the Stars and Stripes – American again. Hornblower experienced the same feeling of exasperated impotence which he had known in the old days of his service under Pellew. What was the use of blockading a coast, and enduring all the hardships and perils of that service, if neutral vessels could sail in and out with impunity? Their cargoes of wheat were officially non-contraband, but wheat was of as vital importance to Bonaparte as ever was hemp, or pitch, or any other items on the contraband list – the more wheat he could import, the more men he could draft into his armies. Hornblower found himself drifting into the eternal debate as to whether America, when eventually she became weary of the indignities of neutrality, would turn her arms against England or France – she had actually been at war with France for a short time already, and it was much to her interest to help pull down the imperial despotism, but it was doubtful whether she would be able to resist the temptation to twist the British lion's tail.

The new arrival, smartly enough handled, was edging in now to the quay. A backed topsail took the way off her, and the warps creaked round the bollards. Hornblower watched idly, Bush and Brown beside him. As the ship was made fast, a

127

gangplank was thrown to the quay, and a little stout man made ready to walk down it from the ship. He was in civilian clothes, and he had a rosy round face with a ridiculous little black moustache with upturned ends. From his manner of shaking hands with the captain, and from the very broken English which he was speaking, Hornblower guessed him to be the pilot.

The pilot! In that moment a surge of ideas boiled up in Hornblower's mind. It would be dark in less than an hour, with the moon in its first quarter – already he could see it, just visible in the sky high over the setting sun. A clear night, the tide about to ebb, a gentle breeze, southerly with a touch of east. A pilot available on the one hand, a crew on the other. Then he hesitated. The whole scheme was rash to the point of madness – beyond that point. It must be ill-digested, unsound. His mind raced madly through the scheme again, but even as it did so he was carried away by the wave of recklessness. There was an intoxication about throwing caution to the winds which he had forgotten since his boyhood. In the tense seconds which were all he had, while the pilot was descending the gangplank and approaching them along the quay, he had formed his resolution. He nudged his two companions, and then stepped forward and intercepted the fat little pilot as he walked briskly past them.

'Monsieur,' he said. 'I have some questions to ask you. Will you kindly accompany me to my ship for a moment?'

The pilot noted the uniform, the star of the Legion of Honour, the assumed manner.

'Why, certainly,' he said. His conscience was clear; he was guilty of no more than venal infringements of the Continental system. He turned and trotted alongside Hornblower. 'You are a newcomer to this port, Colonel, I fancy?'

'I was transferred here yesterday from Amsterdam,' answered Hornblower, shortly.

Brown was striding along at the pilot's other elbow; Bush was bringing up the rear, gallantly trying to keep pace with them, his wooden leg thumping the pavement. They came up to the

Witch of Endor, and made their way up her gangplank to her deck; the officer there looked at them with a little surprise. But he knew the pilot, and he knew the customs uniform.

'I want to examine one of your charts, if you please,' said Hornblower. 'Will you show us the way to the cabin?'

The mate had not a suspicion in the world. He signed to his men to go on with their work and led the way down the brief companion to the after cabin. The mate entered, and politely Hornblower thrust the pilot in next, before him. It was a tiny cabin, but there was sufficient room to be safe when they were at the farther end. He stood by the door and brought out his two pistols.

'If you make a sound,' he said, and excitement rippled his lips into a snarl, 'I will kill you.'

They simply stood and stared at him, but at last the pilot opened his mouth to speak – speech was irrepressible with him.

'Silence!' snapped Hornblower.

He moved far enough into the room to allow Brown and Bush to enter after him.

'Tie 'em up,' he ordered.

Belts and handkerchiefs and scarves did the work efficiently enough; soon the two men were gagged and helpless, their hands tied behind them.

'Under the table with 'em,' said Hornblower. 'Now, be ready for the two hands when I bring 'em down.'

He ran up on deck.

'Here, you two,' he snapped. 'I've some questions to ask you. Come down with me.'

They put down their work and followed him meekly, to the cabin where Hornblower's pistols frightened them into silence. Brown ran on deck for a generous supply of line with which to bind them and to make the lashings of the other two more secure yet. Then he and Bush – neither of them had spoken as yet since the adventure began – looked to him for further orders.

'Watch 'em,' said Hornblower. 'I'll be back in five minutes with a crew. There'll be one more man at least to make fast.'

He went up to the quay again, and along to where the gangs

of galley slaves were assembling, weary after their day's work of unloading. The ten chained men under the sergeant whom he addressed looked at him with lack-lustre eyes, only wondering faintly what fresh misery this spruce colonel was bringing them.

'Sergeant,' he said, 'bring your party down to my ship. There is work for them there.'

'Yes, Colonel,' said the sergeant.

He rasped an order at the weary men, and they followed Hornblower down the quay. Their bare feet made no sound but the chain which ran from waist to waist clashed rhythmically with their stride.

'Bring them down on to the deck,' said Hornblower. 'Now come down into the cabin for your orders.'

It was all so easy, thanks to that uniform and star. Hornblower had to try hard not to laugh at the sergeant's bewilderment as they disarmed him and tied him up. It took no more than a significant gesture with Hornblower's pistol to make the sergeant indicate in which pocket was the key of the prisoners' chain.

'I'll have these men laid out under the table, if you please, Mr Bush,' said Hornblower. 'All except the pilot. I want him on deck.'

The sergeant and the mate and the two hands were laid out, none too gently, and Hornblower went out on deck while the others dragged the pilot after him; it was nearly quite dark now, with only the moon shining. The galley slaves were squatting listlessly on the hatchcoaming. Hornblower addressed them quietly. Despite his difficulty with the language, his boiling excitement conveyed itself to them.

'I can set you men free,' he said. 'There will be an end of beatings and slavery if you will do what I order. I am an English officer, and I am going to sail this ship to England. Does anyone not want to come?'

There was a little sigh from the group; it was as if they could not believe they were hearing aright – probably they could not.

'In England,' went on Hornblower, 'you will be rewarded. There will be a new life awaiting you.'

Now at last they were beginning to understand that they had not been brought on board the cutter for further toil, that there really was a chance of freedom.

'Yes, sir,' said a voice.

'I am going to unfasten your chain,' said Hornblower. 'Remember this. There is to be no noise. Sit still until you are told what to do.'

He fumbled for the padlock in the dim light, unlocked it and snapped it open – it was pathetic, the automatic gesture with which the first man lifted his arms. He was accustomed to being locked and unlocked daily, like an animal. Hornblower set free each man in turn, and the chain clanked on the deck; he stood back with his hands on the butts of his pistols ready in case of trouble, but there was no sign of any. The men stood dazed – the transition from slavery to freedom had taken no more than three minutes.

Hornblower felt the movement of the cutter under his feet as the wind swung her; she was bumping gently against the fends-off hung between her and the quay. A glance over the side confirmed his conclusions – the tide had not yet begun to ebb. There were still some minutes to wait, and he turned to Brown, standing restless aft of the mainmast with the pilot sitting miserably at his feet.

'Brown,' he said quietly, 'run down to our boat and bring me my parcel of clothes. Run along now – what are you waiting for?'

Brown went unhappily. It seemed dreadful to him that his captain should waste precious minutes over recovering his clothes, and should even trouble to think of them. But Hornblower was not as mad as might appear. They could not start until the tide turned, and Brown might as well be employed fetching clothes as standing fidgeting. For once in his life Hornblower had no intention of posing before his subordinates. His head was clear despite his excitement.

'Thank you,' he said, as Brown returned, panting, with the canvas bag. 'Get me my uniform coat out.'

He stripped off his colonel's tunic and put on the coat which

Brown held for him, experiencing a pleasant thrill as his fingers fastened the buttons with their crown and anchor. The coat was sadly crumpled, and the gold lace bent and broken, but still it was a uniform, even though the last time he had worn it was months ago when they had been capsized in the Loire. With this coat on his back he could no longer be accused of being a spy, and should their attempt result in failure and recapture it would shelter both himself and his subordinates. Failure and recapture were likely possibilities, as his logical brain told him, but secret murder now was not. The stealing of the cutter would attract sufficient public attention to make that impossible. Already he had bettered his position – he could not be shot as a spy nor be quietly strangled in prison. If he were recaptured now he could only be tried on the old charge of violation of the laws of war, and Hornblower felt that his recent exploits might win him sufficient public sympathy to make it impolitic for Bonaparte to press even that charge.

It was time for action now. He took a belaying pin from the rail, and walked up slowly to the seated pilot, weighing the instrument meditatively in his hand.

'Monsieur,' he said, 'I want you to pilot this ship out to sea.'

The pilot goggled up at him in the faint moonlight.

'I cannot,' he gabbled. 'My professional honour – my duty –'

Hornblower cut him short with a menacing gesture of the belaying pin.

'We are going to start now,' he said. 'You can give instructions or not, as you choose. But I tell you this, monsieur. The moment this ship touches ground, I will beat your head into a paste with this.'

Hornblower eyed the white face of the pilot – his moustache was lop-sided and ridiculous now after his rough treatment. The man's eyes were on the belaying pin with which Hornblower was tapping the palm of his hand, and Hornblower felt a little thrill of triumph. The threat of a pistol bullet through the head would not have been sufficient for this imaginative southerner. But the man could picture so clearly the crash of the belaying pin upon his skull, and the savage blows which would beat him to death, that the argument Hornblower had selected was the most effective one.

'Yes, monsieur,' said the pilot, weakly.

'Right,' said Hornblower. 'Brown, lash him to the rail, there. Then we can start. Mr Bush, will you take the tiller, if you please?'

The necessary preparations were brief; the convicts were led to the halliards and the ropes put in their hands, ready to haul on the word of command. Hornblower and Brown had so often before had experience in pushing raw crews into their places, thanks to the all-embracing activities of the British pressgangs, and it was good to see that Brown's French, eked out by the force of his example, was sufficient for the occasion.

'Cut the warps, sir?' volunteered Brown.

'No. Cast them off,' snapped Hornblower.

Cut warps left hanging to the bollards would be a sure proof of a hurried and probably illegal departure; to cast them off meant possibly delaying inquiry and pursuit by a few more minutes, and every minute of delay might be precious in the uncertain future. The first of the ebb was tightening the ropes now, simplifying the business of getting away from the quay. To handle the tiny fore-and-aft rigged ship was an operation calling for little either of the judgement or of the brute strength which a big square rigger would demand, and the present circumstances – the wind off the quay and the ebbing tide – made the only precaution necessary that of casting off the stern warp before the bow, as Brown understood as clearly as Hornblower. It happened in the natural course of events, for Hornblower had to fumble in the dim light to disentangle the clove hitches with which some French sailor had made fast, and Brown had completed his share long before him. The push of the tide was swinging the cutter away from the quay. Hornblower, in the uncertain light, had to time his moment for setting sail, making allowance for the unreliability of his crew, the eddy along the quayside, the tide and the wind.

'Hoist away,' said Hornblower, and then, to the men, 'Tirez.'

Mainsail and jib rose, to the accompaniment of the creaking

of the blocks. The sails flapped, bellied, flapped again. Then they filled, and Bush at the tiller – the cutter steered with a tiller, not a wheel – felt a steady pressure. The cutter was gathering way; she was changing from a dead thing to a live. She heeled the tiniest fraction to the breeze with a subdued creaking of her cordage, and simultaneously Hornblower heard a little musical chuckle from the bows as her forefoot bubbled through the water. He picked up the belaying pin again, and in three strides was at the pilot's side, balancing the instrument in his hand.

'To the right, monsieur,' gabbled the individual. 'Keep well to the right.'

'Port your helm, Mr Bush. We're taking the starboard channel,' said Hornblower, and then, translating the further hurried instructions of the pilot, 'Meet her! Keep her at that!'

The cutter glided on down the river in the faint moonlight. From the bank of the river she must make a pretty picture – no one would guess that she was not setting forth on some quite legitimate expedition.

The pilot was saying something else now; Hornblower bent his ear to listen. It had regard to the advisability of having a man at work with the lead taking soundings and Hornblower would not consider it for a moment. There were only Brown and himself who could do that, and they both might be wanted at any moment in case it should be necessary for the cutter to go about – moreover, there would be bound to be a muddle about fathoms and metres.

'No,' said Hornblower. 'You will have to do your work without that. And my promise still holds good.'

He tapped his palm with the belaying pin, and laughed. That laugh surprised him, it was so blood-curdling in its implications. Anyone hearing it would be quite sure that Hornblower was determined upon clubbing the pilot to death if they went aground. Hornblower asked himself if he were acting and was puzzled to discover that he could not answer the question. He could not picture himself killing a helpless man – and yet he could not be sure. This fierce, relentless determination that

134

consumed him was something new to him, just as it always was. He was aware of the fact that once he had set his hand to a scheme he never allowed any consideration to stop his carrying it through, but he always looked upon himself as fatalistic or resigned. It was always startling to detect in himself qualities which he admired in other men. But it was sufficient, and satisfactory, for the moment, to know that the pilot was quite sure that he would be killed in an unpleasant fashion if the cutter should touch ground.

Within half a mile it was necessary to cross to the other side – it was amusing to note how this vast estuary repeated on a grand scale the characteristics of the upper river, where the clear channel serpentined from shore to shore between the sandbanks. At the pilot's warning Hornblower got his motley crew together in case it might be necessary to go about, but the precaution was needless. Closehauled, and with the tide running fast behind her, the cutter glided across, Hornblower and Brown at thesheets, and Bush at the tiller demonstrating once more what an accomplished seaman he was. They steadied her with the wind again over her quarter, Hornblower anxiously testing the direction of the wind and looking up at the ghostly sails.

'Monsieur,' pleaded the pilot, 'monsieur, these cords are tight.'

Hornblower laughed again, horribly.

'They will serve to keep you awake, then,' he said.

His instinct had dictated the reply; his reason confirmed it. It would be best to show no hint of weakness towards this man who had it in his power to wreck everything – the more firmly the pilot was convinced of his captor's utter pitilessness the less chance there was of his playing them false. Better that he should endure the pain of tight ligatures than that three men should risk imprisonment and death. And suddenly Hornblower remembered the four other men – the sergeant and the mate and the two hands – who lay gagged and bound in the cabin. They must be highly uncomfortable, and probably fairly near to suffocation. It could not be helped. No one could be spared for a moment from the deck to go below and attend to them. There

135

they must lie until there was no hope of rescue for them.

He found himself feeling sorry for them, and put the feeling aside. Naval history teemed with stories of recaptured prizes, in which the prisoners had succeeded in overpowering weak prize crews. He was going to run no risk of that. It was interesting to note how his mouth set itself hard at the thought, without his own volition; and it was equally interesting to observe how his reluctance to go home and face the music reacted contrariwise upon his resolution to see this affair through. He did not want to fail, and the thought that he might be glad of failure because of the postponement of the settlement of his affairs only made him more set in his determination not to fail.

'I will loosen the cords,' he said to the pilot, 'when we are off Noirmoutier. Not before.'

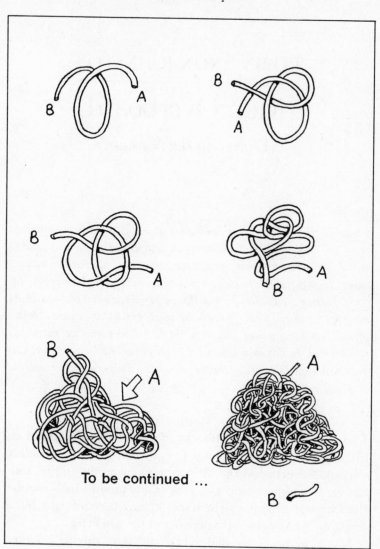

To be continued ...

Bill Beavis, from *Yachting Monthly*

ROBIN KNOX-JOHNSTON

Man Overboard

(From *Last But Not Least*)

I think of all the things that can happen at sea, losing a man overboard is one of the most frightening. In theory the actions and manoeuvres to take to recover the person are quite simple, but every so often something occurs to make things difficult, and the fact that a life is at risk makes everyone a bit tense. During the 1977–78 round-the-world-race, we had planned what to do in the Southern Ocean if anyone fell overboard, but the sheer suddenness of such an event means that even the best laid plans are not always remembered. In this case, which I described in my book on the race, Last But Not Least, *the crew behaved splendidly, and we were fortunate that it all happened in daylight.*

I have never liked the 13th day of the month, although I tell myself that being a rational human being I am not super-stitious. Nevertheless the 13th always worries me a little, and I am very cautious on Friday, 13th of any month. In November the 13th was a Sunday, which should have been all right, but in fact it gave us our worst experience of the whole leg.

Just after noon, we had gybed and were tidying up after-wards, the spinnaker filled and the lazy guy tautened up under Bill who was leaning overside setting the main boom guy. It happened so quickly that he did not have time to pull himself back and he was flung into the air and fell back into the sea. Fortunately, the accident was seen, and someone yelled 'man overboard' immediately. We had the spinnaker and full main up at the time and were making about 10 knots in a force 5 following wind and rather lumpy sea, which had been easing slowly since the last gale half a day before. I was standing in the cockpit and jumped to the port rail to see Bill's startled face pass beneath me. Julian tried to throw a line but it tangled, and the major, who was aft, grabbed a lifebuoy and threw it to him. It landed about five feet away from him, and he swam towards it and pulled it beneath him to provide support.

Bill's first reaction was one of surprise, then he tried to grab the hull, but there was nothing to grip. He does not remember grabbing the lifebuoy, but as the boat sailed away, he could at least console himself with the thought that he had been seen. Back on board we were letting fly the spinnaker sheet and guy and trying to bring the boat round into the wind whilst the crew poured on deck and began to heave down the spinnaker. I posted three lookouts whose sole task was to watch Bill who was by now about a cable astern. Although he was disappearing behind the swell waves, he was visible when on top of them, his yellow oilskins showing up particularly well. Peter, who was on the helm, had started the engine, and was trying to motor us round but the boat's head would not come up through the wind, and the spinnaker had come back against the mast and was helping to hold us back. We swung off to clear the spinnaker and when it flew out astern we hauled it in aft, but the boat would still not come round. Eventually we realized that although the engine was running in gear the propeller was not turning. Julian leaped down to check the gear box, and I got a party organized to get a headsail up so that we could sail back if necessary. A yell from Peter stopped us – the propeller shaft was turning. 'Oh Christ,' I thought, 'we've lost the propeller.' Bill had been in the water for about five minutes by now, and I was beginning to worry that if we did not get to him soon, the cold would kill him. We had drifted further from him, and he was not so easy to pick out two to three cables away, but we knew his general whereabouts because the seabirds had gathered over him, the same way they had collected over an injured seal a few days before.

We were working feverishly to get the yankee set, when Peter called out to us again. He had us motoring at last. What must have happened was that the propeller, which is of the folding type, had seized closed through lack of use since leaving Cape Town, but by revving the engine up Peter had created enough centrifugal force to open it up. We headed back towards Bill at full throttle, rolling alarmingly in the sea until we got the mainsail organized, and as we got closer, I was relieved to see that Bill was still conscious. I conned Peter up to weather of Bill, and we stopped a yard clear of him and three of us leaned over the side and hauled him up. Desperation must have lent strength to us, because Bill is very solidly built and weighs fifteen stone, and normally we could never have done it, even if his clothes had not been waterlogged.

As we hustled Bill below to the doctor, I told Peter to get us back on course, and get the spinnaker ready to hoist again. The Doc stripped off Bill's clothing, and he was vigorously towelled, whilst his hand, which was cut when he went in, was bandaged up. Apart from being very cold, and the cut hand, he was none the worse for his experience. We had been incredibly lucky. On the previous race, three men had fallen overside in the Southern Ocean and all three had drowned. I said a very heartfelt prayer of gratitude, and thanked my lucky stars that I was sailing with a good crew, because their response had been magnificent. I have never lost a man at sea, although this was the second time I had had one go overside, and it was one record I was determined to maintain.

Once I had seen that Bill was OK, I went back on deck to find us still lying head to wind. Peter was fiddling with the engine controls, and the engine stopped suddenly on us. We soon found the reason. When we had stopped to pick Bill up, a rope staysail sheet had gone overside and was now firmly caught round the propeller. There is only one way of dealing with this sort of problem: someone has to go into the water with a knife, and cut the rope clear. I looked around desperately for a volunteer, anyone who might save me from having to go into that freezing water, but everyone was suddenly doing something vital. The previous time I had had to dive in the Southern Ocean I had gone in naked to repair the rudder on *Suhaili*. The moment I had jumped in, the cold had taken my breath away, and I had realized that my breathing was getting faster and shallower and I was not going to last very long. This time I put on a wet suit, and socks on my feet, and then gently lowered myself into the water. It was freezing. How Bill had survived ten minutes I could not think, and he reckoned that he could have lasted about twenty minutes more. I duck-dived under the hull and had a look. The sheet was twisted round and round the propeller, and it took two attempts to unravel the end. I then went under again and tried to pull the jam clear, but the rope was held firmly between the propeller box and the 'P' bracket. I had hoped to save the sheet, but as it was so tightly jammed it had to be cut, and Julian passed me down a knife. By this time I could not really feel my hands, but they grasped the handle and seemed to have the knife firm. It took two attempts to get the rope clear and check that the propeller was OK and then I was hauled on board. Someone was very kindly waiting on deck with a large glass of brandy, which made me feel better. My body was OK where the wet suit had protected it, but my face, hands and feet were completely numb.

Once I was back on board, Peter, who had been holding the boat hove-to whilst I fiddled around underneath, paid off, and got us back on course, and reset the spinnaker. Once we were under way again we took stock of the situation. Bill was off deck for a while with a cut hand, but was otherwise fine. David Alan-Williams had been thrown into the whip aerial by the spinnaker guy which had bruised him and put him on light duties for a couple of days, but it broke the whip aerial. We had a shortened staysail sheet, too short for use, so we rove another, and a couple of stanchions had been bent. Later, on the slipway in Auckland, we also discovered that the 'P' bracket was bent out of true about five inches, but we did not realize it at the time. All in all we had come out of it all very lightly, and I think we were incredibly lucky.

The inevitable question was whether Bill would have gone in

if he had had safety harness clipped on. The answer is probably that he would not have, but I think he would have been very badly injured. The spinnaker exerts a great deal of pull, and the guy, having tightened up, would have lifted him until his harness took the weight, and then slipped up the front of his body and onto his neck and face. As it happens, we probably had less to worry about because he had gone in, than if he had been harnessed on board. Whether he should have been harnessed is a matter of opinion. We did wear harnesses and used them a lot of the time, and in particular when it was blowing up. Had the wind been stronger and the seas higher, Bill would have been clipped on, but would probably have done the job in a different way anyway.

I think in retrospect that there was a lot we could have done differently to get him back sooner. First, the spinnaker, sheets, guys and halyards should have been let go completely, so that the sail blew clear of the boat and left us unencumbered. If it had floated we could have picked it up later, but if not it would just have had to be sacrificed. Secondly, if we had had some sort of a line coiled on each quarter that could be thrown overside to a man in the water, there is a chance he would catch it and be much closer to the boat once we stopped. It is almost impossible to pull oneself up a line onto a boat if the boat is travelling at more than 5 knots, but if there was a bowline in the end of the line, at least the person could hang on. It does not take all that long to luff the boat up into the wind and bring her to a halt; it is turning round that takes the time. Thirdly, I think that boats with folding propellers should run them briefly twice a week to prevent them sticking. Our propeller refusing to open cost us more time than anything else. If the weather conditions had been worse, it would have taken a lot longer to get the boat under control and stop her, and having thrown one lifebuoy out, we would have had to throw another over shortly afterwards so that we had something else to follow back to the man in the water. But we only had two lifebuoys.

I had had a four-man liferaft put just behind the helmsman for just this sort of emergency, but in the event no one thought to throw it over. Neither did we throw over the marker buoy because with all its clutter of lights, drogues, dye markers and so on, it just could not be cleared away quickly enough. For the right reasons, yacht safety equipment has been made too complicated, and this negates its effectiveness. The simplest safety item to throw over was a lifebuoy, and it worked. Other safety equipment wants to be as easy to release and throw.

One aspect of the day's events was that I had now two of the crew unfit to work in their watches. It made matters somewhat easier that Bill and David were in different watches, but we could not run a watch with only five people. To get over the problem, we cancelled the cook's schedule, and David and Bill became full-time cooks until they were fit to work again. It was a bit unfair on them, but the boat had to be sailed. Neither liked it very much, and after two days David was passed fit and Bill said that he was OK as well. I gave Bill a rope to hold, took the other end myself, and told him to pull. He tried, and attempted to hold back his wince, but it was obvious that his hand needed a bit longer to recover, and he had to cook for another day before he could pull on a rope safely!

DOUGAL ROBERTSON

Day Seven

(From *Survive the Savage Sea*)

In the summer of 1972 the 39-foot schooner Lucette, *sailing from the Galapagos to the Marquesas, was holed by killer whales and sank almost immediately. Her owners, the Robertsons, their three sons and a student friend, took to the liferaft and towed with them the yacht's 9-foot dinghy. They survived in the liferaft for two weeks but when this became untenable they moved to the dinghy, and, amazingly, managed to live in it for a further three weeks before being picked up by a Japanese fishing boat. That they managed to survive for so long was almost certainly at least in part due to the fact that he was a master mariner and she a state registered nurse, ideal qualifications for coping with such a disaster. Their story, later related by Dougal Robertson in his book,* Survive the Savage Sea, *is one of courage, endurance and skill. I found it totally riveting. Deservedly, it became a best seller when it was published in 1973 and must be recommended reading for anyone venturing on a trans-ocean passage. There have been many stories published about survival at sea but the Robertsons' book is a classic of the genre. It is so well written and so evocative that any extract from it would probably convey their predicament and how they dealt with it. I have chosen day seven because that was when the unrelenting will to survive became uppermost in Dougal Robertson's mind.*

The windless night filled our ears with unaccustomed silence, and in the quiet of the calm swell the phosphorescent gleam of the large dorado, streaking from under the raft and leaping high into the air, to land in bursting showers of green glowing fire, was a display not often seen by men.

The foul dryness of our mouths aggravated the discomfort of our sleepless bodies as we tried to ease the agony of our thirst, twisting this way and that, then breathlessly we watched the gathering clouds obscure the stars and as dawn paled the eastern horizon, it began to rain, a heavy shower this time, with a steady downpour. Slowly the water in the pipe from the canopy ran clear and we filled our empty cans and spare plastic bags, our bellies and our mouths until we could not force down another drop. We lay with our faces turned to the sky and let the pure fresh water cleanse the salt from our beards and hair; suddenly everything had changed from the shadow of the spectre of death to the joyful prospect of life, and all by a shower of rain. We would make the Doldrums now! We lay uncaring, chewing strips of dorado and revelling in the absence of thirst, talking excitedly of good food and watching the bulging plastic bags swing lazily from the roof of the canopy. We had water!

Douglas, lazily watching the dispersing clouds, suddenly sat up with a start, pointing excitedly. 'A ship! A ship! It's a ship!' We all crowded to the door of the raft, staring in the direction of his pointing finger; a cargo vessel of about six thousand tons was approaching us on a course that would bring her within three miles of us. I felt my heart pound against my ribs. 'Get out the flares,' I said hoarsely, 'and pass them to me in the dinghy, they'll see us better from there.'

Three miles was a fair distance, but on a dull day like this, against a background of rain, they should see us easily. I clambered into the dinghy and Douglas passed me the rockets and hand flares; my hands trembled as I ripped open a parachute rocket flare and, with a mute appeal to the thing to fire, struck the igniter on the fuse. It spluttered and hissed, then roared off on a trajectory high above the raft, its pinkish magnesium flare slowly spiralling downwards leaving a trail of smoke in the sky. They couldn't fail to see it. I waited a moment or two watching for the ship to alter course, then struck a hand flare, holding it high above my head. The blinding red light was hot to hold and I pointed it away from the wind to ease my hand, the red embers of the flare dropping into the dinghy; as it went out I struck another, smoke from the first now a rising plume in the sky; surely they must see that. I waited a little, my hands trembling. 'This chance might not come again,' I said, anxious faces crowding the door of the raft, 'I'm going to use our last rocket flare and one more hand flare.' We watched tensely as the second rocket flare soared and spiralled its gleaming distress message high above us; desperately I struck the third hand flare and held it high, standing on the thwart and holding onto the mast. 'Look, look, you bastards!' I shouted. 'Set fire to the sail!' Lyn's voice. I stuck the flare to the sail but it only melted. The ship sailed on, slowly disappearing behind a rain shower, and when she reappeared her hull was half obscured by the horizon, five miles distant and disappearing fast. The time was eleven o'clock. My shoulders drooped. 'We daren't use another,' I said. 'They won't see it now and we have to keep something for the next one.' We had three hand flares left. Lyn smiled cheerfully. 'It says in the instruction book that the first one probably wouldn't see us,' she said slowly, 'and I'd already told the twins not to expect anything.' She gathered the twins to her, comfortingly. We stared at the dwindling speck on the horizon and felt so lonely that it hurt. 'I'm sorry lads.' I felt very tired. 'We used to consider that one of the most important tenets of good seamanship was 'Keep a good lookout'. That lot seem to be pretty poor seamen!'

Our position was 3° north and 240 miles west of Espinosa (almost 95° 20′ W) on Wednesday, 21 June, midsummer's day, on the route from Panama to the Marquesas; the ship was westbound. I surveyed the empty flare cartons bitterly, and the one smoke flare which was damp and wouldn't work, and something happened to me in that instant that for me changed the whole aspect of our predicament. If these bloody seamen couldn't rescue us, then we would have to make it on our own and to hell with them. We would survive without them, yes, and that was the word from now on, 'survival', not 'rescue', or 'help', or dependence of any kind, just survival. I felt the strength flooding through me, lifting me from the depression of disappointment to a state of almost cheerful abandon. I felt the bitter aggression of the predator fill my mind. This was not our environment and the beasts around us would eat us if we failed. We would carve a place for ourselves among them; they had millions of years of adaptation on their side, but we had brains and some tools. We would live for three months or six months from the sea if necessary, but 'We would get these boys to land' as Lyn had said, and we would do it ourselves if there was no other way. From that instant on, I became a savage.

We lunched on dry fish, a half biscuit and a tiny piece of glucose each to cheer us up, followed by a good mouthful of water, after which I returned to the *Ednamair* to clear up the debris of empty cases and burnt powder. When I returned to the raft I said: 'From now on we have a new password; we forget words like rescue for we can expect none, and think of existence only in terms of survival.' Lyn nodded immediately. 'What's the password for today?' she called to the twins – 'Survival' they echoed, and they seemed to understand that it was no longer a question of 'if' we would reach land, but 'when'. Robin seemed to regard our change of attitude with mild indifference, but in Douglas's eyes I could see that the shadow of the ship's passing would haunt him for the rest of his days.

The wind rose from the south again after the passage of rain and I decided to stream the sea anchor, to hold the raft in the shipping route, for forty-eight hours. I was tempted to carry straight on but rescue is, after all, part of the survival exercise and I would at least pay lip service to the ordinary practices of seamen. In two days the current would have carried us beyond the shipping lane and we could then proceed on our voyage to the coast. The sea anchor streamed and the sail reefed, I had just returned to the raft when an excited call from Sandy, watching the sea anchor's mushroom trailing behind us, brought us to the after door of the raft. A huge hammerhead shark glided six feet below, its wicked eye leering up at us. The twins gazed down at it fascinated, not in the least afraid, and discussed its more dangerous man-eating practices with

Douglas as dispassionately as if they were visiting an aquarium on an afternoon outing.

Towards late afternoon we felt an unusually hard bump on the raft floor, unlike the quick thrust of the striking dorado, and poking our heads out of the stern door of the raft we found ourselves gazing at the large scaly head of a turtle, protruding eyes set above a nasty-looking beak, surveying us with a dispassionate unblinking scrutiny. The day before I would have said, 'Leave it, we can't manage that,' but now things were different. 'We'll have this one,' I said. 'Let's get it aboard the dinghy.' The turtle's flippers had become entangled in the sea anchor line, so first passing a rope from the dinghy under the raft, we made it fast to one of the back flippers, then, carefully avoiding the searching beak, freed the turtle from the sea anchor rope and towed it around the raft to the *Ednamair*. I scrambled onto the dinghy and pulled the now struggling turtle alongside, reaching down to grasp the back flippers. I twisted the turtle round until its back was next to the dinghy and heaved. It was surprisingly heavy and as it came aboard, the dinghy tilted alarmingly. I threw my weight to the other side to trim her, then with a bump and a thrashing of claws the reptile lay on its back in the bottom of the dinghy, all eighty pounds of it. I put my thumbs up to the twins and Douglas watching from the raft, and they cheered excitedly.

Now for the difficult bit. I looked at the armoured amphibian with a farmer's eye; where to cut to reach the artery? I had helped to slaughter a few pigs and lambs and had a pretty good idea how to tackle this one. I grasped the pointed knife in my right hand and, putting a foot on each of the front flippers, held its beak with my left hand, then plunged the knife into the leathery skin of the neck, deep into the spinal column, then with quick, outward strokes of the knife to right and left I cut both vein and artery. Deep red blood spurted into the bottom of the dinghy and gradually, beak and flippers ceased thrashing as the beast died. Apart from a few minor scratches I was unscathed, so in the gathering dusk I washed the blood from my hands into the bottom of the dinghy, careful not to spill any in the water. I didn't want to bring any inquisitive sharks around, especially our hammerheaded friend, until we had started moving again, for if they suspected that the blood came from the raft they would probably attack the inflatable with disastrous consequences. Excitedly we discussed this addition to our larder. Lyn had heard from someone that turtle livers were inedible so we decided to discard the offal rather than risk illness. Twenty-four hours previously I would not have had the stomach for such a bloody business but the laws of survival applied and the first principle, 'The fittest survive, the weakest go to the wall', had now become our way of life. We would struggle and endure and if our reflexes were not as swift as the animals and fish around us, we had cunning, and we would improve with practice.

The wind steadily increased during the evening and the sea became noisy about the raft again. Inside, bodies twisted and turned restlessly seeking a comfortable position, for only the twins were small enough to lie down full length on the floor. Water slopped around the depressions made by hip-bones and elbows in the inflated rubber flooring and the sound of the watchkeeper blowing up the flotation chambers became just another sound in the night to those who tried to rest. To the watchkeeper, it was an exhausting routine of bailing and blowing which left the mouth sore, the hands cramped and the tiny pimples, forerunners of salt-water boils, stinging on hands, feet, legs, arms and buttocks. We sometimes found time to look around for ships!

Broker's Jargon

(From *Yachting Monthly*)

Former yacht-broker Hugh Marriott, troubled by conscience these past three years, finally speaks out and confesses the truth of the phrases that used to flavour his adverts:

Well below today's replacement cost: thoroughly overpriced for a boat built in 1946

Seakindly: slow

Character yacht: ugly

Uncluttered by berths: no accommodation

Easy-to-handle rig: undercanvased

Two mainsails: one was made in 1946

Full set of flares: they were all made in 1946

Classic lines: boat was built in 1846

Quiet engine: petrol

We know this boat very well: we have actually seen this one

o.n.o.: even the owner knows he won't get what he is asking

ALISTAIR MACLEAN

Finale

(From *HMS Ulysses*)

Alistair MacLean is, of course, one of the postwar wonders of the book world. His novels have been best sellers in a whole variety of languages, and he's a highly successful screenwriter, too. But my favourite, still, is his first book, HMS Ulysses, *which was an immediate and immense success when it was published in 1955. I remember that time only too well as I was studying for my entry exams for the Royal Navy, and instead of working I read this extraordinarily gripping documentary novel of an Arctic convoy to Russia during the Second World War. If it wasn't for Alistair MacLean perhaps I'd have passed into the Royal Naval College, Dartmouth, and become an officer in the Royal Navy. (I'm actually very pleased now that I didn't!) The piece I've chosen is right at the end of the book where after facing attack after attack by German warships and U-boats in the grimness of the Arctic Sea in winter,* HMS Ulysses *and those of her crew who remain alive, go down fighting in a final effort to save what remains of the convoy. It is a magnificent finish to a magnificent novel and I have found this final scene impossible to forget.*

Hope was rising, rising fast. Less than an hour to go, now, and the battle squadron would be there. It was dark, dark with the gloom of an Arctic storm, and heavy snow was falling, hissing gently into the dark and rolling sea. No plane could find them in this – and they were almost beyond the reach of shore-based aircraft, except, of course, for the Condors. And it was almost impossible weather for submarines.

' "It may be we shall touch the Happy Isles," ' Carrington quoted softly.

'What?' Turner looked up, baffled. 'What did you say, Number One?'

'Tennyson.' Carrington was apologetic. 'The Captain was always quoting him. . . . Maybe we'll make it yet.'

'Maybe, maybe.' Turner was non-commital. 'Preston!'

'Yes, sir, I see it.' Preston was staring to the north where the signal lamp of the *Sirrus* was flickering rapidly.

'A ship, sir!' he reported excitedly. '*Sirrus* says naval vessel approaching from the north!'

'From the north! Thank God! Thank God!' Turner shouted exultantly. 'From the north! It must be them! They're ahead of time. . . . I take it all back. Can you see anything, Number One?'

'Not a thing, sir. Too thick – but it's clearing a bit, I think. . . . There's the *Sirrus* again.'

'What does she say, Preston?' Turner asked anxiously.

'Contact. Sub contact. Green 30. Closing.'

'Contact! At this late hour!' Turner groaned, then smashed his fist down on the binnacle. He swore fiercely.

'By God, she's not going to stop us now! Preston, signal the *Sirrus* to stay. . . .'

He broke off, looked incredulously to the north. Up there in the snow and gloom, stilettos of white flame had lanced out briefly, vanished again. Carrington by his side now, he stared unwinkingly north, saw shells splashing whitely in the water under the bows of the Commodore's ship, the *Cape Hatteras*: then he saw the flashes again, stronger, brighter this time, flashes that lit up for a fleeting second the bows and super-structure of the ship that was firing.

He turned slowly, to find that Carrington, too, had turned, was gazing at him with set face and bitter eyes. Turner, grey and haggard with exhaustion and the sour foretaste of ultimate defeat, looked in turn at his first lieutenant in a long moment of silence.

'The answer to many questions,' he said softly. 'That's why they've been softening up the *Stirling* and ourselves for the past couple of days. The fox is in among the chickens. It's our old pal the *Hipper* cruiser come to pay us a social call.'

'It is.'

'So near and yet . . .' Turner shrugged. 'We deserved better than this. . . .' He grinned crookedly. 'How would you like to die a hero's death?'

'The very idea appals me!' boomed a voice behind him. Brooks had just arrived on the bridge.

'Me, too,' Turner admitted. He smiled: he was almost happy again. 'Have we any option, gentlemen?'

'Alas, no,' Brooks said sadly.

'Full ahead both!' Carrington called down the speaking tube: it was by way of his answer.

'No, no,' Turner chided gently. 'Full *power,* Number One. Tell them we're in a hurry: remind them of the boasts they used to make about the *Abdiel* and the *Manxman* . . . Preston! General emergency signal: "Scatter: proceed independently to Russian ports." '

The upper deck was thick with freshly fallen snow, and the snow was still falling. The wind was rising again and, after the warmth of the canteen where he had been operating, it struck at Johnny Nicholls's lungs with sudden, searing pain: the temperature, he guessed, must be about zero. He buried his face in his duffel coat, climbed laboriously, haltingly up the ladders to the bridge. He was tired, deadly weary, and he winced in agony every time his foot touched the deck: his splinted left leg was shattered just above the ankle – shrapnel from the bomb in the after mess-deck.

Peter Orr, commander of the *Sirrus,* was waiting for him at the gate of the tiny bridge.

'I thought you might like to see this, Doc.' The voice was strangely high pitched for so big a man. 'Rather I thought you would want to see this,' he corrected himself. 'Look at her go!' he breathed. 'Just look at her go!'

Nicholls looked out over the port side. Half a mile away on

the beam, The *Cape Hatteras* was blazing furiously, slowing to a stop. Some miles to the north, through the falling snow, he could barely distinguish the vague shape of the German cruiser, a shape pinpointed by the flaming guns still mercilessly pumping shells into the sinking ship. Every shot went home: the accuracy of their gunnery was fantastic.

Half a mile astern on the port quarter, the *Ulysses* was coming up. She was sheeted in foam and spray, the bows leaping almost clear of the water, then crashing down with a pistol-shot impact easily heard, even against the wind, on the bridge of the *Sirrus*, as the great engines thrust her through the water, faster, faster, with the passing of every second.

Nicholls gazed, fascinated. This was the first time he'd seen the *Ulysses* since he'd left her and he was appalled. The entire upperworks, fore and aft, were a twisted, unbelievable shambles of broken steel: both masts were gone, the smoke-stacks broken and bent, the director tower shattered and grotesquely askew: smoke was still pluming up from the great holes in fo'c'sle and poop, the after turrets, wrenched from their mountings, pitched crazily on the deck. The skeleton of the Condor still lay athwart 'Y' turret, a Stuka was buried to the wings in the fo'c'sle deck, and she was, he knew, split right down to the water level abreast the torpedo tubes. The *Ulysses* was something out of a nightmare.

Steadying himself against the violent pitching of the destroyer, Nicholls stared and stared, numbed with horror and disbelief. Orr looked at him, looked away as a messenger came to the bridge.

'Rendezvous 1015,' he read. '1015! Good lord, twenty-five minutes time! Do you hear that, Doc? Twenty five minutes time!'

'Yes, sir,' Nicholls said absently: he hadn't heard him.

Orr looked at him, touched his arm, pointed to the *Ulysses*.

'Bloody well incredible, isn't it?' he murmured.

'I wish to God I was aboard her,' Nicholls muttered miserably. 'Why did they send me –? Look! What's that?'

A huge flag, a flag twenty feet in length, was streaming out below the yardarm of the *Ulysses,* stretched out taut in the wind of its passing. Nicholls had never seen anything remotely like it: the flag was enormous, red and blue and whiter than the driving snow.

'The battle ensign,' Orr murmured. 'Bill Turner's broken out the battle ensign.' He shook his head in wonder. 'To take time off to do that *now* – well, Doc, only Turner would do that. You knew him well?'

Nicholls nodded silently.

'Me, too,' Orr said simply. 'We are both lucky men.'

The *Sirrus* was still doing 15 knots, still headed for the enemy, when the *Ulysses* passed them by a cable length away as if they were stopped in the water.

Long afterwards, Nicholls could never describe it all accurately. He had a hazy memory of the *Ulysses* no longer plunging and lifting, but battering through waves and troughs on a steady even keel, the deck angling back sharply from a rearing forefoot to the counter buried deep in the water, fifteen feet below the great boiling, tortured sea of white that arched up in seething magnificence above the shattered poopdeck. He could recall, too, that 'B' turret was firing continuously, shell after shell screaming away through the blinding snow, to burst in brilliant splendour over and on the German cruiser: for 'B' turret had only star-shells left. He carried, too, a vague mental picture of Turner waving ironically from the bridge, of the great ensign streaming stiffly astern, already torn and tattered at the edges. But what he could never forget, what he would hear in his heart and mind as long as he lived, was the tremendous, frightening roar of the great boiler-room intake fans as they sucked in mighty draughts of air for the starving engines. For the *Ulysses* was driving through the heavy seas under maximum power, at a speed that should have broken her shuddering back, should have burned out the great engines. There was no doubt as to Turner's intentions: he was going to ram the enemy, to destroy him and take him with him, at a speed of just on or over 40 incredible knots.

Nicholls gazed and gazed and did not know what to think: he

felt sick at heart, for that ship was part of him now, his good friends, especially the Kapok Kid – for he did not know that the Kid was already dead – they, too, were part of him, and it is always terrible to see the end of a legend, to see it die, to see it going into the gulfs. But he felt, too, a strange exultation; she was dying, but what a way to die! And if ships had hearts, had souls, as the old sailing men declared, surely the *Ulysses* would want it this way too.

She was still doing 40 knots when, as if by magic, a great gaping hole appeared in her bows just above the waterline. Shellfire, possibly, but unlikely at that angle. It must have been a torpedo from the U-boat, not yet located: a sudden dip of the bows could have coincided with the upthrust of a heavy sea forcing a torpedo to the surface. Such things had happened before: rarely, but they happened. . . . The *Ulysses* brushed aside the torpedo, ignored the grievous wound, ignored the heavy shells crashing into her and kept on going.

She was still doing 40 knots, driving in under the guns of the enemy, guns at maximum depression, when 'A' magazine blew up, blasted off the entire bows in one shattering detonation. For a second, the lightened fo'c'sle reared high into the air: then it plunged down, deep down, into the shoulder of a rolling sea. She plunged down and kept on going down, driving down to the black floor of the Arctic, driven down by the madly spinning screws, the still thundering engines her own executioners.

FRANK SNOXELL

Sayings of Sinbad

(From *The Yachtsman's Bedside Book*)

Be the wind 'twixt west and north
'Tis better not to sally forth.
When it blows 'twixt north and east
The sea's not fit for man or beast.
Should it come 'twixt east and south
Remain within the harbour mouth.
And anywhere 'twixt south and west
Delay departure – home is best.
But should there be no wind at all
Tie up your ship against the wall.

COLIN MUDIE

How to Cut a Rig

(From *The Yachtsman's Bedside Book*)

I've known Colin Mudie ever since I went to him in 1967 to design me a yacht in which to go round the world. He came up with a magnificent creation, a 53-footer to be built in steel for a very reasonable price, but unfortunately I could not raise the money so I went in Suhaili. *I was introduced to Colin through a friend who recommended him highly because Colin, he told me, was always prepared to turn his hand to something different. This obviously applies to Colin's writing just as much as it does to his profession as a yacht designer, and I think this amusing article proves his versatility with his pen. I've always been interested in the derivation of nautical terms and I think Colin's come up with a very original theory for some of them!*

Once upon a time, long years ago, a great naval architect lounged contentedly on the quarterdeck of his latest and greatest creation. Months, years, even centuries, it felt like, of work lay behind him. Acres of paper covered with inspired doodlings, thousands of envelopes scribbled on and gallons of coffee drunk. Years of juggling with skysails and studdingsails and ringtails and watersails, months of intricate model tests with royals and topgallants in stiff card and spiders' webs of cotton tracing the runs of billethead and bobstay, buntline and brace.

At last, he said, gazing with pride about him, at last the *full rigged ship.*

Just at that moment, however, a vicious squall, hidden from the helmsman by the leach of the spanker, came howling out of the otherwise clear sky. The full rigged ship groaned and lurched as it struck, the groan hardening into a splintering and a crashing as the mizzen squaresails gave to the furious blast. Mizzen skysail tumbled on mizzen royal, and mizzen royal tumbled on mizzen topgallant and topsail and the whole lot fell into the sea to leeward tearing with them the cro'jack.

Now seafaring men are not noted for forbearance and humility in time of stress, and the great designer was but human, deep down that is.

'*Barque*,' he swore.

The tail of the first squall struck at the mainmast, now exposed to the full fury of the elements. The main course was the first to go, leaving but mizzen spanker and jigger and the main spencer standing aft of the mainmast.

'*Jackass barque*,' he swore again.

For a moment there was a respite, but even while he struggled to brush the ruins of the mizzen upper topgallant halliard from his beard the storm clouds gathered all around.

Another howling squall struck to the thunder of frapping canvas and splintering of spars.

'*Barquentine*,' he yelled when it seemed that the remaining square yards on the main were doomed, but instead the mizzen mast was first to go.

'Oh, *Brig!*' he swore, going purple in the face. Another squall and a rending of hemp and canvas.

'*H*rm*phr*d*t* Brig!*' raged the great man, fairly dancing with rage and quite oblivious to the presence of ladies. Another howling puff and,

'*Brigantine!!*' and yet another relentless blow struck.

'*Topsail schooner!!!*' shouting the strongest oath he knew back at the elements, fairly frothing at the mouth by now with temper. But they were not to be daunted even by such an eloquent verbal castigation as this, and if anything they were incensed and their fury increased. Squalls blew up all around the compass, vying with each other to strike a blow at this manmade thing which offended the gods with its perfection. Shrewd blow followed shrewd blow at the rigging remaining.

'*Schooner*,' moaned the great man as more gear flew away.

'*Ketch*,' he could but groan as the main topmast departed through the murk. A momentary revival of spirit had him shouting '*Cutter!*' as the mainmast went, but as blow followed blow he wept.

'*Sloop*,' he mumbled into his beard as the jib blew away; and as the last great gust cleared the decks completely all that was to be heard in the stillness which followed was but a sad sobbing and gulping of, '*Hulk*.'

As the sun came out of the cleaned blue sky that follows a gale, the yachting journalist who was present for these trials reached for his notebook and, while they were still clear in his mind, noted down all the great man's words, assuming in his innocence that these new and strange oaths were but the type names of the various rigs passed through during the tempest.

There are, it is only proper to report, some other theories on the why and wherefore of the naming of the various combinations of sail once to be seen. Undoubtedly some are derived, but the great weight of circumstantial evidence is overwhelmingly on our side if you stop to consider the names given in other languages to these same rigs. What else but similar circumstances to those described above would result in the names?

Our French naval architect, probably trying to get his development trials in during one of those rare dashes out of Toulon, obviously had a somewhat similar experience. It may have been that his craft had a more Gallic delicacy than our Anglo-Saxon, or it may be that the mistral strikes with a more sudden and terrible fury. In any case, poor chap, he had even less time to express himself on the subject.

There he was, just rolling the fine phrase *un trois mâts carré* around his tongue and into his cognac when the very word *carré* was blown off the end, leaving him, as it were, barque rigged. Somewhat startled, he began again, only to gulp with surprise at another crash of sail and spar. '*Un trois mâts goelette*.' But Frenchmen are made of fiery stuff and he had time to deliver a quick opinion as the next blow struck – '*Un veritable brick*,' he marvelled. But then the senselessness of all this destruction got him in the pit of his logic and he swore low French oaths as crash followed crash.

'*Brigantin*,' he shouted at the sky, followed by '*Goelette*,' '*Ketch*,' and '*Cotre*.' By this time his moustache had gone and he had chewed halfway through his beard, which may account for '*un sloop*' and the final muffled '*un ponton*' as he gave up ship design until the cessation of hostilities.

The Spanish were also a great seafaring people, and your Señor Don is no man to allow himself to be disarranged and generally discommoded without a few pungent words about the situation. To this day, Spanish seamen use such bitten off epithets as *Barga*, *Bergantin*, and even *Bilandra* to commemorate the occasion.

The further you look into this question of the etymological derivations of strange seafaring words the more certain it is that the great majority of them fall into two distinct classes. Some came from the characters of the seamen who manned the vessels rather than from any particular peculiarity of the vessel itself. The second have names belonging to some imperfect understanding or perfect misunderstanding, as often and principally occurs between seamen of different races.

For examples of the first kind we do not have to look far. The *Brighton Hog Boat*, for instance. As far as it is possible to trace, they were not named out of pride in a particular type of pig farmed locally. Nor were the boats themselves more than just a little like the couchant hog in appearance, although they were well set up and aldermanical craft with nicely rounded corporations and a dignified spritsail ketch rig as often as not. No, one is left with a suspicion that the brave sailormen who manned them were of a gluttonous disposition and not particularly well liked by their poorer neighbours, the *Deal Hovellers*, for instance, or the *Hastings Luggers*.

Even closer at home perhaps we might consider the traditional *Thames Peter* boat. There is a splendid and romantic story of how they were named out of gratitude to St Peter himself for personally consecrating the church that Edward the Confessor built where Westminster Abbey now stands. But the Peter boat in that case might be expected to have reflected the glory with lofty spars and soaring and elegant ends. Instead it was a real cockney of a craft with simple and bold shape and a stumpy little sprit rig, just ideal for dark and slippery work among the old wharves and warehouses. Can it only be coincidence that a safe-breaker is known to this day as a 'Peterman' (after the saltpetre used to blow off the hinges)? What better way to escape from the shorebound Watch or the Peelers than to let the tide waft you away from the turmoil and alarm through the black night to lie low on the Essex flats.

Consider also the number of occasions when whole fishing fleets divided into *Drifter* and *Driver* rigs (as at Lowestoft and down in the West Country). Seamen like everyone else are not perfect. Some are content to let life amble past while others are consumed with energy and ambition. The drifters gravitated naturally to a form of fishing that suited their temperaments, while the drivers, who started more or less equal with the drifters no doubt crammed on more and more sail, chased the fish up and down the Channel and North Sea until, perforce, they became deep-sea trawlermen.

In Scotland, the *Fifie, Zulu, Scaffie, Nabby* and *Baldy* are as unlikely a set of names as you will find. They must be personal references to their owners, for, with the possible exception of the last, it is inconceivable that they are proper technical descriptions of hull form or rig. And then there are the East Coast *Billyboys* and *Dandies*, fat rounded ketches with leeboards, and the Manx *Dandies* and *Nickeys* – full-quartered craft with straight stems, rigged either as ketches or luggers. Nothing, therefore, about their appearance to connect them with their dashing names. It can only have been the smart young chaps who manned them who earned the titles as they came ashore, spruced up to the nines, to frolic and show off before the sober townsfolk.

It is tempting to add the *Flushing Mussel Boat* to this list, also the *Swim Head Eel Catcher,* the *Gorleston Crabber* and the *Lizard*

Longliner. These are each and every one recognizable as sea-faring people known to us all. A more considered look, however, confirms, a little regretfully, that these are, in fact, quite respectable technical names for the vessels concerned – as is the *Itchen Ferry Boat*, although we might all hesitate before spending a night on one of those. *Sardine Lugger* and *Mousehole Drift Boat* are another pair of names which, although perfectly legitimate, are none the less evocative rather of the pertinent aside than a file in the Min. of Ag. and Fish. I wish, how I wish, however, that we could be sure, one way or the other, of the *Old Goole Leeboard Smacks*. Surely any nice young girl would hesitate to risk fate by showing her pretty new necklace to that lot of old gentlemen for a start. And surely no sea captain would risk his ticket by writing in his log, 'We came up with an *Old Goole Leeboard Smack*.'

Our second category, that of the names perpetuated through a misunderstanding, is a fairly amorphous bunch. The size of the mistake varies to almost any degree, making it impossible to have a hard and fast distinction around them. Not all now appear so obvious as the famous error of the Admiral of the Ocean Seas, Columbus, who himself put the West Indies where they are today.

On all voyages of exploration it is essential to have a 'namer' on board. Someone, usually the captain, who instantly and without delay gives a recognizable name to each new sight as it appears over the horizon. Without such an official the voyage would soon collapse in disarray, with the crew reduced to a stuttering inconsequentiality, which would quite spoil the effect of their tall tales of derring-do. Similarly, there must be a diarist or recorder, usually the first mate, who carefully notes all these names so that there can be no argument.

But what happens if the namer has a bad cold? It seems quite likely that the captain of one gallant band setting forth to explore the seas to the south of England was such a sufferer. It would appear that they left in the spring from a south-west harbour, as might be Plymouth. We can draw these conclusions at once because any ship's captain with a stinking cold in the autumn would make certain to lie in the Downs until it was better, and from the record of the first landfall being in St Malo bay. There they sighted a two-masted lugger with not only lug topsails but light upper topsails set as well. What the captain really said we shall never know, but the mate recorded it as a *Bisquine*. A little later a powerful cutter with an early version of the genoa jib set flying was miserably written down as a *Camaret Crabber*. In the Portuguese trades a tiny lateen rigged craft is a *Vigo Fisherman*. In the Tagus they come across *Fregates*, and so this miserable cold is carried south where even the Mediterranean sunshine fails to cure it at once. *Barquettes*, *Tartanes*, and *Bragagnas*, splutters our captain, and even a fine Genoese vessel with three masts, square rigged on the fore and lateen rigged on the others can only raise a *Vinco*. Later, in the Adriatic, a perfectly reasonable lugger with a fine, high-flung bowsprit held on to her port tack too long, to slide past very close to shouts of *Trabacola*. Another, whose only crime was a somewhat insignificant foresail, and, no doubt, a Venetian love of showing off, had *Bragozzi* shouted at her as she passed. Off the Turkish coast a handsome cutter, rather Scandinavian in style, happened to coincide with an explosive sneeze and is now recorded for posterity as a *Tchektirmé*. However, we can at least record that virtue finally prevailed, the victim recovered, and a Turkish Peterboat with a sprit rig and banana ends was greeted with a glad *Caïque*, and the advent of a spritsail ketch-rigged barge was the start of a phase of sober and scientific observations with its naming as a *Constantinople Trader*.

There is perhaps a third category which should be considered in any serious assessment of the essential derivations of the more important nautical names. Paradoxically, it is not yet a recognized branch of marine etymology. It stands in the sciences where perhaps psychology stood a hundred years ago. Known and used by all, but lacking the scientific framework and title to be the subject of special study, formal lectures, and government grants. It might perhaps be considered under the somewhat cumbersome title of the 'Ask a silly question . . .' derivative root. Whether you agree with this title or not, it would appear to affect nautical etymology at a somewhat later period than those we have been considering already.

Of course, it might be that they arrived in common usage from the pompous decks of the John Company's ships – the pot-bellied East Indiamen – but it is most likely that it flourished and was most highly developed during the great days of steam, the liner, and the Peninsular and Oriental Steamship company. In earlier times the passenger afloat was pitched well and truly into shipboard life and could not but acquire some marine knowledge in voyages which might last up to six months or a year. The liners, however, put layers of mahogany, silver and linen insulation between the passengers and the horrors of the deep. This insulation was swept aside only on occasions of direst emergency, and the great majority of passengers moved about the world in the greatest ignorance of things maritime. Thus they became butts for the bored and practical joking mariners, who looked for amusement and entertainment in their off-watch hours. How else can you account for letters home from the Far East telling of *Dhows, Baggaras* and *Sambuks, Naggers, Feluccas, Gharawas,* and *Pattamars* all sailing on the sea?

The Western seaman of the time was an arrogant creature, with all the Victorian assurance of built-in infallibility in a fallible world. From the lofty decks of his iron-built steamer, with its vast smoke stacks belching speed and power above and with its gleaming machinery and elaborate menus below, with its long straight wake disappearing over the horizon behind, he had but one word for the ships of the East whenever the twain did meet at sea or in harbour. He would look with a sneer at the ragged sails, corrugated bamboo spars, leaking decks, painted eyes, and dismiss half the world's transport with but a single word.

'*Junk*, madam,' would say the bearded purser, '*just Junk.*'

RICHARD MAURY

Record Passage

(From 'Curious Records of the Sea')

What is the longest ship's passage on record? In 1890 the schooner Marlborough of Glasgow sailed homeward bound from New Zealand. She failed to arrive. Months passed. She was posted as missing. One, two, three years went by: four – and she was forgotten. But one morning, twenty-four years later, she was sighted off Cape Horn still afloat, still striving against the weather. The vessel was boarded and on the decks and inside the musty cabins were found the crew: silent, bleached, skeletons. Nothing spoke. The mystery stands to this day.

This ship was probably the victim of Antarctic ice which has a way of working northwards along the course that a sailing vessel running east from New Zealand would normally take. Perhaps at this point, one of the breathtaking gales of those latitudes dismasted her, or perhaps she became so surrounded by floating ice that she could not work clear, allowing the pack to hem her in, until, at another season, it froze about her, holding her in this position until the occurrence of a great thaw many years later, when, at last, the prevailing northerly currents brought her out into the light of day.

NEIL HOLLANDER AND HARALD MERTES

Who is the Captain?

(From *The Cook is the Captain*)

For centuries the notion has persisted that the Captain is in charge of his ship. But this is merely a myth, a thin façade of law and custom. The Cook is the Captain, and he always has been.

True, the Captain presents himself as the all-powerful commander who armed with his sextant, tables and telescope assumes responsibility for the ship's course. But with modern technology navigation is hardly a skill. To move from point A to point B today's Captain simply sets the autopilot or wind vane then lazily stares at the sea, dreaming about the days when he had something important to do.

Meanwhile, the Cook labours in his galley, creating not just the next meal, but that special, light-hearted spirit which is so vital to any voyage. For some traditions never die. As always, food at sea is the sailor's strength, his tonic and his joy. And no one knows this better than the Cook. He is the caretaker of the crew's mood, the ship's guardian, mediator and confessor.

Unlike the Captain, who maintains his customary distance, the Cook is intimately involved with all that happens on board. Conflicts, secrets, triumphs, complaints and gossip all pass across his galley table. He knows everyone's likes and dislikes, their foibles, passions and sensitivities. More than anyone else, he is in tune with the pulse of the crew. Delicately balancing the needs of the lovesick, homesick, landsick and seasick, the Cook constructs his menus as though he were trimming the ship.

During a long passage when days are quiet and boredom

silently creeps on board, the smell of cakes, soufflés and chowder rakes the ship, drawing everyone to the galley. With pride and purpose, the Cook welds his crew together. Over platters of steaming delicacies, arguments dissolve and friendship is kindled.

Should a crisis strike – a sudden onshore wind, a fouled anchor or a raging gale – the Cook knows just how much rum to put in each man's grog, and when the Captain's composure begins to crack, the Cook hurries to his side with a well-laced mug of coffee and a few words of encouragement.

Wherever the ship ventures – calm waters or troubled seas – the Cook is always on duty, diligently nourishing his crew. Usually somewhere in the background, his uniform never adorned with rank or decoration, he is unsung in song, verse or prose. But as every sailor knows, *The Cook is the Captain.*

That was the authors' introduction to their book, The Cook is the Captain, *which is full of original recipes. I like their unorthodox attitude! But though they may be overemphasizing the importance of the cook just a bit, meals certainly take on a greater significance at sea, because, apart from the obvious need for regular nourishment to keep up one's energy to sail the boat, mealtimes provide a welcome break for a few minutes from the concentration and hard work. The following recipe is one of my own favourites, but I have yet to find anyone else who will eat it!*

BULLY BEEF CURRY

2 oz butter
1 oz curry powder
2 large onions
1 tin bully beef

2 Oxo cubes
Tabasco sauce
½ lb rice

Melt butter in a pan and then add curry powder and stir well. Then add chopped onions and allow to fry for a couple of minutes, when the sliced corned beef can be stirred in. Cook, stirring well for 5 minutes. Add water to not quite cover the mixture and crumble 2 Oxo cubes into the pan. Stir and bring to the boil, then leave to simmer. A teaspoonful or so of Tabasco sauce or similar pepper or chilli sauce can be added if the Vindaloo version is required.

Boil the rice in sea water. It does not stick that way, and also you are making sure you have a good intake of salt. When the grains feel soft, strain off the surplus water and serve.

My wife, Sue, has an excellent recipe for kedgeree:

1 lb cooked fish	3 hardboiled eggs
2 tablespoons butter	⅓ cup milk
1 tablespoon chopped onion	salt and pepper to taste
2 cups cooked rice	parsley

Flake the fish. Melt butter and gently fry onion, rice, fish, chopped egg whites, and salt and pepper. Add milk and stir over low heat until very hot. Serve garnished with finely chopped egg yolks and parsley.

NAOMI JAMES

Boris

(From *At One With The Sea*)

Women have been sailing single-handed ever since the early 1950s when Ann Davidson crossed the Atlantic alone. But she stopped at the Azores and it was not until 1970 that a woman crossed non-stop on her own. This was Nicolette Milne-Walker and her remarkable achievement was not topped until eight years later when Naomi James sailed alone around the world. Naomi's circumnavigation was a classic voyage, and this attractive, feminine New Zealander has done more to advance female equality than all the bra-burners put together. And she did not just complete the trip, she did it in a very respectable time, stopping only twice, at Cape Town and the Falkland Isles. The extract I've chosen from her book of this voyage called At One With The Sea *is different in mood from the others but it catches extraordinarily well the aloneness of single-handed sailing and the poignancy of losing anything that can offer companionship and a connection, however tenuous, with normal, everyday life.*

On 16 October I crossed the equator, going like a rocket. I'd been especially looking forward to this day because my sister Juliet had put aboard five curious-looking parcels, each marked with the days on which they should be opened. I opened 'Happy First Equator Crossing!' and found a book of short stories by D. H. Lawrence and a sticky lollipop which I immediately ate. Juliet had provided another fifteen or so books to add to my library of 200, but I still wasn't sure if that would be enough. My mother-in-law had given me a fantastic book called

170

Royal Heritage which is fat and full of gorgeous pictures I could dwell upon and so make the book last, whereas most of the books I consumed in a sitting.

I had a *Concise Encyclopaedia of Antiques,* which was fascinating and also time-consuming. Antiques are a passion of mine, and I spent hours day-dreaming of the house I would like to have, and where the Queen Anne furniture would go . . . and the Rembrandts! In addition to this I had brought pieces of wood from which to carve chess pieces, though I planned to leave this pastime till the weather got cold. I also had several books on navigation and astronomy to amuse me.

In honour of my equator crossing at 17.00 I cooked myself a three-course dinner: vegetable soup, beef with boiled potatoes, onions and peas, and pickled red cabbage, and pineapple slices for 'afters'. This was helped down with a small bottle of best French champagne, and my gloom of the previous day disappeared, along with the empty bottle, to the bottom of the ocean!

My kitten Boris also had a share of my dinner and scattered the bits over the chart-room floor as was his usual practice. He looked the picture of a contented cat secure in his own neighbourhood and didn't mind the occasional wild lurch or bang which was so much a part of this strange environment. However, I did shatter his complacency for a moment that afternoon when I dropped the grill pan on the floor close to him. He gazed at me in horror with his fur on end and his mouth full of tuna; I broke the spell by laughing and his hair slowly subsided.

17 OCTOBER (DAY 39)

It is still very hot and as I cannot open the hatches because of the spray it is like a Turkish bath in the cabin. I have then a choice either to steam quietly down below, or to come up on deck and get drenched. My favourite position is on the 'bridge', that is to say standing outside the cabin hatchway with my feet on the cockpit seats. From here I can keep a lookout, hold on against the movement and be reasonably sheltered from the spray.

I brought Boris up to the 'bridge' and held him aloft so he could see the reef I had just put in the mainsail. He reviewed my work, but the wind flattened his ears and that was something he didn't apreciate! I find reefing very much easier now. In fact I feel far more confident about handling sails generally and hope that when bad weather comes I shall be able to avoid the catastrophes that arise from inexperience or bad seamanship. However, if anything does go wrong I feel it will be my fault and not *Crusader's*; she is a marvellous boat and I feel an overwhelming affection for her.

Boris still attempts to walk across the flexible fuel tank. He tries to maintain some dignity, but it is an impossibility while gyrating. I laugh and he looks at me with disdain, then sniffs and stalks off; he doesn't like to be laughed at. He has grown very fussy about his food of late and has insisted on a change of diet. This morning I weakened and gave him some more tuna which he condescended to eat; one of these days you'll be eating corned dog and beans, I told him severely, but he didn't listen.

As I sit in my comfortable seat by the chart table with Edith Piaf singing my favourite French songs and I sip my favourite drink, sweet martini (without the embellishments), I feel a glow of extreme well-being. What's more I've found an excellent tonic for dejection when the weather gets rough – reading a chapter of David Lewis's book, *Ice Bird*! His frightful struggles and his capsize in Antarctica make my journey feel like a summer cruise. I look around and feel I've a long way to go before life becomes that intolerable.

Reading David Lewis reminded me of my own philosophy which I know is trite but still of help to me. It is that when things get bad, they must get better. Situations never stay constant, and sooner or later one snaps out of a black mood and stands up to meet the next problem. But why am I saying this? I've got the whole world, so what have I got to be despondent about?

28 OCTOBER (DAY 50)

Boris and I got a dowsing this morning. When we went on deck I hadn't bothered to put up my oilskin hood, and I took a full dollop of sea down my neck. Boris had been perched on the jib winch and he got it as well. He looked shocked and shook himself, but he didn't remove himself below as I thought he would. He looks so funny when he gallops along the heeling deck with his ears flat and his fur fluffed up, but I'm sure he doesn't mind getting wet. He spends many hours gazing down the cockpit drain watching the bits of flotsam gurgle up and down; every now and again he reaches out a paw and tries to grab a piece, only to find that the water rushes up the drain and all he gets is a wet foot for his pains.

The next morning, at eight o'clock, Boris went over the side.

After a senseless search for two and a half hours I sat down at the chart table and forced myself to write the following:

Boris has gone. I feel numb and unable to think straight, but I'm going to write this down so that I can begin to accept that it has happened and there's nothing more I can do. Nothing. Shortly after breakfast, I was on the foredeck getting the ghoster ready to hoist when I saw him doing his daredevil act of walking on the toerail around the boat's edge. I reached out to pull him back, but he came in voluntarily; then I must have turned away. A few minutes later, out of the corner of my eye, I saw him lurch – as he had done several times before – but this time he went over. I saw him hit the water and I rushed to the stern to disconnect the self-steering gear and put the wheel hard over. Then I dashed to the mast to let go the mainsail and staysail halyards. I could see him in the wake about fifty yards away and *Crusader* was slowly turning around towards him. But then I had to go below to start the engine and although it took only a matter of seconds when I got back to the wheel he had disappeared. When I was past the place where I'd seen him last, I cut the engine, called and listened. There was nothing to be seen or heard. I called and called like a fool and steered the boat round in circles, but it was no use and eventually I told myself to stop. It was so calm and there were barely more than a few ripples on the surface, but Boris was nowhere to be seen.

For a long while afterwards I sat on the stern and just stared at the water, my mind in a turmoil of remorse and my thoughts transfixed by the sheer horror of what had happened. If only I could have found him, I said again and again; there must have been something more I could have done.

After a time I roused myself to go and finish hanking on the ghoster and slowly, reluctantly, hoisted it. With a sense of unreality I watched that sunflecked, seemingly different piece of ocean drift away and finally disappear over the horizon.

GUY ROPE (CAPTAIN)

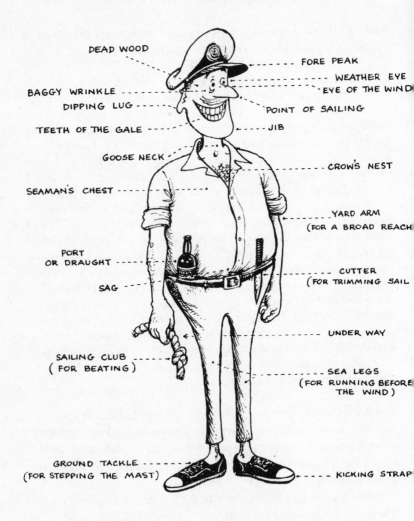

(From *Three Sheets in the Wind* by Norman Thelwell)

MAY DAY (FIRST MATE)

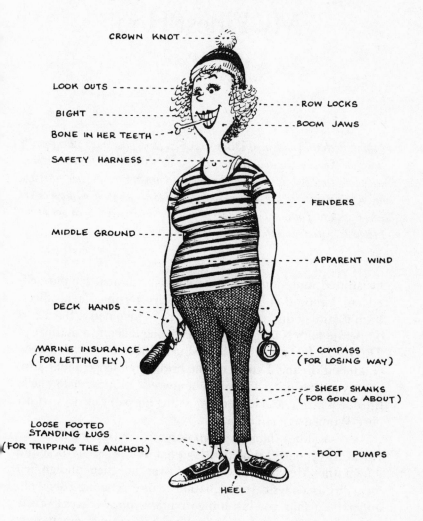

CROWN KNOT

LOOK OUTS

BIGHT

BONE IN HER TEETH

SAFETY HARNESS

ROW LOCKS

BOOM JAWS

FENDERS

MIDDLE GROUND

APPARENT WIND

DECK HANDS

MARINE INSURANCE
(FOR LETTING FLY)

COMPASS
(FOR LOSING WAY)

SHEEP SHANKS
(FOR GOING ABOUT)

LOOSE FOOTED
STANDING LUGS
(FOR TRIPPING THE ANCHOR)

FOOT PUMPS

HEEL

(From *Three Sheets in the Wind* by Norman Thelwell)

175

RICHARD GORDON

My Finest Hour

(From *Punch*)

I think Richard Gordon, of Doctor at Sea *fame plus many other equally funny books, is a hilarious writer. I knew he actually had been a doctor at sea at one time but didn't know the details. Then in* Punch *some years ago he daringly revealed how he was launched onto his seagoing medical career – not with a splash but a stagger – and it's always remained one of my favourite stories. So here it is.*

Frustrated ambitions are essential nourishment for our self-esteem. I know that I should have made a terrible Naval officer. I am totally undisciplined and bad at trigonometry. But I was desperate for a Naval career, since being taken to a matinee of *The Middle Watch* at the Shaftesbury Theatre in 1929. In my childhood dreams I stood on the bridge, telescope under arm, quietly mastering such perils as shipwreck, mutiny, yellow jack, fire down below, and icebergs, quelling the panic on deck with a curt 'Women and children first.'

As disabilities (largely psychosomatic) barred me from the Royal Navy, once I qualified I settled for the second-best and joined the Merchant one. There was no such undignified formality as a physical examination before becoming a doctor in a merchant ship, you just hung round the lines' offices like any other unemployed sailor. As no British vessel over ninety-nine souls aboard is allowed to sail without a medical officer, and as at that time just after the war ships' doctors had suddenly become as scarce as Liberal MPs, the first office I tried pretty well Shanghaied me on the spot.

My ship was apparently rather older than myself, and had already finished one useful life ferrying soldiers and sahibs to India. She was now about to leave for Australia with some five hundred passengers, middle-class refugees from Mr Attlee's brave new world. I was too jubilant to worry about the vessel's amenities, or even seaworthiness, as they instructed me to join her at Victoria Docks in a week's time. Then they sent me to the shipping registry in the Minories, which I found to combine the atmosphere of a busy post office and a police station on a Saturday night, where someone looked up the *Register* to see if I was a proper doctor, fingerprinted me, and took my photograph with a number in a frame under my chin. This turned out nearer my conception of Jack the Ripper than Jack Tar, but I was compensated with an identity card officially describing me as a 'seafarer'. After my childhood fantasies, it was comparable with actually driving the Flying Scotsman or shooting the winning goal at Wembley.

Doctors employed by Leadenhall Street rather than the Admiralty are obliged to find their own gear, but unhappily, like all newly qualified ones, my financial lifeblood was sadly anaemic. The long-desired blue uniform was bought for two pounds in a pub, from a friend just demobilized as a surgeon-lieutenant. I thought the scuffed gold braid and trail of pink-gin stains down the front gave it a satisfyingly deep-water look. The high-necked tropical 'whites' came second-hand from a theatrical costumers, and had doubtless appeared in several amateur productions of *The Middle Watch*. I found a chauffeur's cap in Soho, added the tie which I kept for funerals, put it all on, and looked in the mirror. To my own eyes, I was as much a sailor as Nelson on top of his column.

The exciting morning arrived for me to go aboard. I said an early farewell to my landlady in Pimlico, picked up my suitcase (which I referred to as my 'ditty-box'), and took the Tube to Canning Town. Only then did misgivings assail me. The Royal Navy provides its medical officers with elaborate instruction to

177

adapt themselves to the physical and social hazards of their new environment. The rougher Merchant Service runs on the principle that once aboard the lugger everything will somehow work itself out. I realized that I didn't know the difference between starboard and leeward, I couldn't tell a chronometer from a dog-watch, and I was equally ignorant of the precise functions of the capstan and the captain. But timidity faded as I stumbled across the dockside railway lines and caught sight of the thin, upright funnels of my ship, poking above the warehouses. I already felt beckoning those empty blue horizons which had enticed Sir Francis Drake and Captain Cook. With the tide (that seemed the phrase) I should be heading for the open sea and the Antipodes.

I hurried up a steep, insecure-looking gangway. At the top sat an old man, smoking a pipe. I announced that I was the new ship's doctor. He hauled up his trouser leg and invited my opinion on his knee. I suggested aspirin, and demanded to see the officer of the watch. He said I could try the cabins under the bridge, mate, but he reckoned everyone was having breakfast.

I found a young man in his pyjamas, shaving in a glass surrounded by photographs of bulbous nudes. To be on the safe side, I saluted smartly. He looked surprised, and offered me a pink gin, which I later discovered to be the more normal form of salutation aboard. He explained that he was the third officer, and to get rid of me suggested that I toured the ship.

As I wandered aft, I first noticed that the vessel was largely in pieces. The decks were cluttered with pipes, girders, sliced ventilators, riveted plates, and quite substantial sections of machinery. Instead of sailors, the ship was alive with arc-welders and carpenters. Instead of bos'n's pipes, there came the periodic scream of tortured metal. I looked over the side. No sea. No oil-streaked threshold of the oceans. Just concrete, a disconcertingly long way below. We were in dry dock, as incapable of sailing to Australia as the Houses of Parliament.

We stayed there for six weeks. They were the finest of my life. I was being paid at generous ocean-going rates. I drew my ration of duty-free tobacco and gin. I ate magnificent meals –

seafarers always do themselves well, perhaps in compensation for eighteenth-century privations. In the evenings, I caught the tube back to my Pimlico haunts. Wearing my uniform, exclusively drinking pink gin, I expanded heartily in my favourite pubs on the joys and hardships of a sailor's life. I began to imagine that from nine to five every day I was really outward bound for Sydney, though there seemed no possibility of even the most able marine engineer ever putting my ship together again.

But one morning the bits were fitted together somehow, smoke came from the funnels, stewards roamed in clean white jackets, winches rattled, flags flew, the captain paced the bridge, and my spirits fell. I loved being a sailor. But I didn't want to go to sea at all. It would be noisy and draughty, and I should certainly be seasick. Even in dry dock I felt definitely queasy. And boat drill would be held as we reached the storm-tossed waters of the Channel. It is always punctual aboard British vessels, because we are as a nation rather good at shipwrecks, lovingly remembering some splendid ones in our history, when everyone drowned with impeccable manners and undampened good humour. As I could hardly jump ship before we had even left port, I should be standing the next morning by my lifeboat, in full view of the passengers, disgracing myself.

I had a cruel choice. I could try and see out boat drill by thinking fixedly of some terrestrial feature like the Albert Hall. Or I could be a coward, and take some seasickness pills. I hesitated until the alarm bells sounded, then fell. Unfortunately, like most in the ship's hospital, the label on the bottle had long ago become unreadable, so I swallowed a handful and hoped for the best.

I stood on deck, cap at a rakish angle, facing the greenish passengers in their lifejackets. I was beautifully eupeptic. The image of myself as a seafarer, which could so easily that morning have been shattered beyond repair, at last came into full focus with my childish vision. If I had cheated, that mattered less and less as the passengers steadily slumped and wilted. I was a sailor, the deck might heave, but I didn't.

But in my haste I had forgotten my basic pharmacology, that an overdose of the drug hyoscine in seasick pills could induce disturbances of vision, staggering, disorganized behaviour, incoherent speech, and outbursts of wild laughter. For the rest of the voyage the passengers pointedly avoided me professionally or socially, and the captain kept trying to smell my breath. A humiliating sequel to a fine moment, I thought bitterly at the time. But the wound healed. It hardly took more than a couple of voyages before I discovered that a ship's doctor drunk at nine in the morning was a matter far less worthy of knowing comment than one being seasick down his brass buttons.

ROBIN KNOX-JOHNSTON

Christmas near the Horn in *Suhaili*

(From *A World of My Own*)

Christmas is very much a family festival at home or on board ship, and indeed my last eleven Christmasses had been spent on BI ships. The thought of being by myself at Christmas rather ruffled me. For almost the first time since I left Falmouth I felt that I was missing something, and that perhaps it was rather stupid to spend one whole year of one's life stuck out on one's own away from all the comforts and attractions that home offers. By now, Dad and my brothers would have brought in logs from the old trees in the garden, and the family would be clustered round a roaring fire in the drawing room, and thinking of getting ready to go to midnight service at the village church in Downe. I recalled winter evenings at home when we played bridge. The memory of Mother as my partner humming 'Hearts and Flowers' and Diana asking Father if she could go 'Crash' or 'Slosh' had me roaring with laughter. The warmth and fellowship of those scenes seemed to be in such contrast to my present circumstances that I brought out a bottle of whisky, feeling that if I couldn't have the fire I could at least give myself an inner glow.

Two glasses later I clambered out on deck and perched myself on the cabin top to hold a carol service. I sang happily away for over an hour, roaring out all my favourite carols, and where I had forgotten the words, singing those I did know over again. By the time I had exhausted my repertoire and had had a few encores I was feeling quite merry. Christmas, I reflected as

I turned in, had got off to a good start after all.

The first words in my diary for 25 December are 'Awoke feeling very thick-headed.' Despite this, at 9 a.m. I drank to those at home where the time was 6 p.m. and then began preparing a currant duff. I made an effort over Christmas lunch. I fried a tin of stewed steak and had potatoes and peas, cooked separately for a change, and to go with them I opened the bottle of wine that brother Mike had given me and which I had been saving for this occasion. I rather overestimated on the quantity though, and this filled me up, so the duff had to wait until the evening before I could tackle it, by which time it had gone soggy.

At 3 p.m. my time I drank a loyal toast, wishing that I had been up early enough to hear the Queen's Speech at 6 a.m. my time. Somehow, gathering together to listen to this speech adds to the charm of Christmas. One becomes aware of people all over the world held by the same interest listening as well, and it makes the world seem a lot smaller. I wished that it was!

In the evening I tried without success to call up New Zealand and Chilean radio stations; then I listened in to some American commercial stations that were coming through rather well. There must have been unusual radio conditions as I was able to pick up local stations from Illinois, Texas and California, and it was on the last that I heard a recording from the 1968 manned American moon shot. I had not heard before of Apollo 8 and her crew, the first men actually to go round the moon, and it gave me food for thought. There they were, three men risking their lives to advance our knowledge, to expand the frontiers that have so far held us to this planet. The contrasts between their magnificent effort and my own trip were appalling. I was doing absolutely nothing to advance scientific knowledge; I would not know how to. Nothing could be learned of human endurance from my experiences that could not be learned more quickly and accurately from tests under controlled conditions. True, once Chichester and Rose had shown that this trip was possible, I could not accept that anyone but a Briton should be the first to do it, and I wanted to be that Briton. But nevertheless to my mind there was still an element of selfishness in it. My mother, when asked for her opinion of the voyage before I sailed, had replied that she considered it 'totally irresponsible' and on this Christmas Day I began to think she was right. I was sailing round the world simply because I bloody well wanted to – and, I realized, I was thoroughly enjoying myself.

JOSHUA SLOCUM

An Amateur Shipwreck

(From *Sailing Alone Around the World*)

*Captain Joshua Slocum is well known for his voyage around the world
alone, the first time the world was circumnavigated single-handed.
Though he was, of course, a hardened professional Yankee shipmaster, he,
like Chichester, only took up yachting late in life.* Sailing Alone
Around the World, *is, as Arthur Ransome rightly says in his introduction to one of its modern editions, 'one of the immortal books', yet
Slocum often rather dismisses the sailing aspects of his voyage. For
instance, it takes him less than one page to describe a seventy-two day
passage across the Pacific. On the other hand, the book is full of dry
comments about the people he meets and the places he visits. Who has not
heard of his encounter with barefoot savages off Tierra del Fuego, and
how he got rid of them by the simple expedient of sprinkling tacks all over
his decks? This little piece I've chosen describes his meeting with a yacht
off the east coast of Australia, and I have selected it because of the
amusement the antics of its crew caused Slocum — and me. He did not have
much time for the 'more-money-than-sense' sailor as his scornful description
of this 'amateur shipwreck' shows.*

I had just finished reading some of the most interesting of the old
voyages in woe-begone ships, and was already near Port
Macquarie, on my own cruise, when I made out, 13 May, a
modern dandy craft in distress, anchored on the coast. Standing
in for her, I found that she was the cutter yacht *Akbar,** which

*Akbar was not her registered name, which need not be told.

184

had sailed from Watson's Bay about three days ahead of the *Spray*, and that she had run at once into trouble. No wonder she did so. It was a case of babes in the wood or butterflies at sea. Her owner, on his maiden voyage, was all duck trousers; the captain, distinguished for the enormous yachtsman's cap he wore, was a Murrumbidgee* whaler before he took command of the *Akbar*; and the navigating officer, poor fellow, was almost as deaf as a post, and nearly as stiff and immovable as a post in the ground. These three jolly tars comprised the crew. None of them knew more about the sea or about a vessel than a newly born babe knows about another world. They were bound for New Guinea, so they said; perhaps it was as well that three tenderfeet so tender as those never reached that destination.

The owner, whom I had met before he sailed, wanted to race the poor old *Spray* to Thursday Island en route. I declined the challenge, naturally, on the ground of the unfairness of three young yachtsmen in a clipper against an old sailor all alone in a craft of coarse build; besides that, I would not on any account race in the Coral Sea.

'*Spray*, ahoy!' they all hailed now. 'What's the weather goin' t'be? Is it a-goin' to blow? And don't you think we'd better go back t' r-r-refit?'

I thought, 'If ever you get back, don't refit,' but I said: 'Give me the end of a rope, and I'll tow you into yon port farther along; and on your lives,' I urged, 'do not go back round Cape Hawk, for it's winter to the south of it.'

They purposed making for Newcastle under jurysails; for their mainsail had been blown to ribbons, even the jigger had been blown way, and her rigging flew at loose ends. The *Akbar*, in a word, was a wreck.

'Up anchor,' I shouted, 'up anchor, and let me tow you into Port Macquarie, twelve miles north of this.'

'No,' cried the owner, 'we'll go back to Newcastle. We missed Newcastle on the way coming; we didn't see the light, and it was not thick, either.' This he shouted very loud, ostensibly for

*The Murrumbidgee is a small river winding among the mountains of Australia, and would be the last place in which to look for a whale.

my hearing, but closer even than necessary, I thought, to the ear of the navigating officer. Again I tried to persuade them to be towed into the port of refuge so near at hand. It would have cost them only the trouble of weighing their anchor and passing me a rope; of this I assured them, but they declined even this, in sheer ignorance of a rational course.

'What is your depth of water?' I asked.

'Don't know; we lost our lead. All the chain is out. We sounded with the anchor.'

'Send your dinghy over, and I'll give you a lead.'

'We've lost our dinghy, too,' they cried.

'God is good, else you would have lost yourselves,' and 'Farewell' was all I could say.

The trifling service proffered by the *Spray* would have saved their vessel.

'Report us,' they cried, as I stood on – 'report us with sails blown away, and that we don't care a dash and are not afraid.'

'Then there is no hope for you,' and again 'Farewell.'

I promised I would report them, and did so at the first opportunity, and out of humane reasons I do so again. On the following day I spoke the steamship *Sherman*, bound down the coast, and reported the yacht in distress and that it would be an act of humanity to tow her somewhere away from her exposed position on an open coast. That she did not get a tow from the steamer was from no lack of funds to pay the bill: for the owner, lately heir to a few hundred pounds, had the money with him. The proposed voyage to New Guinea was to look that island over with a view to its purchase. It was about eighteen days before I heard of the *Akbar* again, which was on 31 May, when I reached Cooktown, on the Endeavour River, where I found this news:

May 31, the yacht *Akbar*, from Sydney for New Guinea, three hands on board, lost at Crescent Head; the crew saved.

So it took them several days to lose the yacht, after all.

NICHOLAS MONSARRAT

The Blocked Oil Pipe

(From *The Cruel Sea*)

In my opinion The Cruel Sea *must rank as one of the great classic sea stories of all time. Grim it undoubtedly is, pessimistic even, but it gripped me totally when I first read it, and it has lost nothing on rereading. How astounding it now seems that Monsarrat felt he had failed as a novelist, for none of his previous books had been particularly successful. He was living in South Africa at the time and had decided to give up writing if* The Cruel Sea *was not a success. It was his twelfth book and he had been writing for eighteen years. 'There was not a paragraph in it which had not been written and rewritten four or even five times,' he records in his autobiography. 'Into it had gone more alcohol, sweat, semen, hopeless misery, sad music, and grinding determination than anything in my life before.' Yet he had no idea he had written a best seller and had to borrow money for his publicity trip to the United States and England when the book was published! We shared the same publisher, Cassell, and I met him at the launch of the first volume of his novel,* The Master Mariner. *Later, he sent me a copy of it and inscribed on the flyleaf: 'To Robin Knox-Johnston – the other Master Mariner', which I thought typically generous of the man. One of the great features about* The Cruel Sea, *of course, is the tension the author manages to maintain throughout, and to illustrate his ability to keep his reader in suspense I have chosen a piece from the middle of the book where* Compass Rose *is forced to a halt in mid-Atlantic for repairs. Lying there helpless, will she get away with it or will a U-boat find an easy victim?*

On the sixth day of their journey home, late in the forenoon watch, Chief ERA Watts came up to the bridge with a worried frown on his face. So far, things had been going well with their return convoy: there had been no shadowing aircraft, no scares about U-boats waiting for them, no drama of any sort. It made a nice change. . . . But now there was a chance of things not going well at all, and it was he who had to break the news.

'Captain, sir!' Watts stood at the back of the bridge, awkwardly shifting his feet on the smooth white planking. He never came up there if he could help it, because it made him feel entirely out of place: his proper station was on the engine-room 'plate' three decks below, among the pipes and the gauges that he understood so well; this open-air stuff, with lookouts and flag signals and water dashing past all round, was not his cup of tea at all. Even his overalls and oily canvas shoes looked funny, with everyone else dolled up in sea boots and duffle coats. . . . Ericson, who had been preparing to check their noon position, and enjoying the sunshine at the same time, turned round at the sound of his voice.

'Well, Chief? Anything wrong?'

'Afraid so, sir.' Watts came forward, rubbing his hands on his overalls. His grey creased face was full of concern. 'I've got a bearing I don't like the feel of at all. Running hot, it is – nearly red hot. I'd like to stop and have a look at it, sir.'

'Do you mean the main shaft, Chief?' Ericson knew that his knowledge of the engine room, sufficient for normal purposes, did not include all the technical refinements, and he wanted to get his facts straight.

'Yes, sir. Must be a blocked oil pipe, by the look of it.'

'Any good if we slow down? I don't want to stop if we can help it.'

Watts shook his head vigorously. 'If we keep the shaft turning it's liable to seize up, sir. And I can't trace the oil line back from the main feed unless we stop engines. It's one of those awkward corners – the after bearing, right up against the gland space.'

Ericson, struggling to give form to the sketchy picture in his mind, frowned in concentration. But the answer seemed fairly clear. If a main bearing were running hot, it wasn't getting its proper ration of oil: if the oil were continuously denied, and the melting point of the metal were reached, the bearing and the surrounding sleeve would be welded into one, and the main shaft would be locked. That was, comparatively speaking, a straightforward piece of mechanical mystery. . . . For a moment he cast about in his mind for possible alternatives, but he knew there were none. They would have to do the least healthy thing in the war at sea – stop in mid-ocean, with their engine put out of commission.

'All right, Chief,' said Ericson, making up his mind to it. 'I'll send a signal, and then ring down for you to stop. Be as quick as you can.'

'I'll be that, sir.'

They were just in visual touch with *Viperous*, who was zig-zagging in broad sweeps across the van of the convoy. When *Compass Rose* signalled her news, the answer was laconic: 'Act independently. Keep me informed.'

'Acknowledge,' said Ericson briefly to Rose, who was signal-man of the watch. Then: 'Starboard ten. Stop engines,' he called down to the wheel house; and *Compass Rose*, turning in a wide sweep away from the convoy, lost way and came gradually to a standstill.

Up on the bridge they waited in silence, while the convoy steamed past them, and the corvette which had the stern posi-tion altered course to pass close by, like an inquisitive terrier which does not know whether to wag its tail or to bark. Down below in the engine room, Watts and a leading stoker called Gracey set to work on their examination of the oil feed. It was indeed an awkward corner, jammed up against a bulkhead and barely approachable: to trace the trouble they had to pick out the suspect oil pipe, from an array of a dozen others, and then take it to pieces in sections to find out which part of it was blocked. The engine room was very hot: they were forced to bend nearly double as they worked, groping for the joints from opposite sides of the piping because there was not room for them to stand side by side: sections of the pipe could not be brought out and examined before other sections of other pipes had been loosened and removed. It was a full two hours before they had located the trouble – an L-shaped, curved section which appeared to be totally blocked.

Watts stepped backwards and straightened up, holding the pipe in one hand and wiping his sweaty forehead with the other. 'Now what?' he said rhetorically. 'How do we find out what's inside this?'

'Suck it and see, I suppose,' answered Gracey, who was a lower-deck comedian of some note.

'Get a piece of wire,' said Watts coldly. Some people were allowed to be funny to Chief ERAs, but leading stokers were not included in this licensed category. 'Not too thick. . . . I'm going up to report to the Captain.'

After two more hours of steady work they were still no further on. Whatever had got inside the pipe seemed to be stuck there immovably: it couldn't be blown out, it couldn't be pushed through, it couldn't be melted or picked to pieces. Waiting on the bridge of his useless ship, Ericson found it hard to restrain himself from storming down to the engine room and telling them to stop loafing and get on with it; but he knew that this would have been futile, as well as unfair. Watts was doing his best: no one else on board could do better. At four o'clock, with the last ships of the convoy out of sight below the horizon, Ericson had sent a signal by R/T to *Viperous*, explaining what was happening; there had been no answer beyond a bare acknowledgement, and it was clear the *Viperous* was setting him a good example in trusting him to make the best of the repair and to rejoin as soon as possible.

He stood wedged in a corner of the bridge, staring down at the dark oily water which reflected the overcast sky; behind him, Ferraby and Baker, who had the watch, were idly examining the pieces of a Hotchkiss anti-aircraft gun which one of the gunnery ratings was stripping. The asdic set clicked and pinged, monotonously wakeful, the radar aerial circled an invisible horizon: the two lookouts occasionally raised their binoculars and swept through their respective arcs – forward, aft, and forward again. *Compass Rose* was entirely motionless: her ensign hung down without stirring, her vague shadow on the water never moved or altered its outline. She was waiting for two things – for her engine to start again, and for the other thing which might happen to her, without warning and without a chance of defending herself either. Who knew what was below the surface of the dark sea, who knew what malevolent eye might be regarding them, even at this moment? In the nervous and oppressive silence, such thoughts multiplied, with nothing to set against them save the hope of getting going again.

On the quarterdeck aft, some of the hands were fishing. If Ericson had told them that they were fishing in at least a thousand fathoms of water, as was in fact the case, it would probably have made no difference. Fishing – even with bread-crumb bait dangling six thousand feet above the ocean bed – was better than doing nothing, at a moment like this.

Down below in the engine room, Chief ERA Watts had come to a certain decision. It involved considerable delay, and some danger of wrecking everything beyond repair; but there was no choice left to him.

'We'll have to saw the pipe up,' he said to Gracey, at the end of another futile bout of poking and picking at the obstruction. Bit by bit, till we find the stoppage.'

'What then?'

'Clear it out, and then braze the whole thing together again.'

'Take all night if we do that,' said Gracey sulkily.

'Take all the war if we don't,' retorted Watts. 'Get a hacksaw, while I tell the Captain.'

Watts was actually up on the bridge when *Viperous* appeared in sight again. She came storming down from the north-westwards at about five o'clock in the afternoon, her big signal lamp flickering as soon as she was over the horizon; she wanted to know everything – the state of their repairs, the chances of their getting going again, and whether they had had any suspicious contacts or seen any aircraft during their stoppage. In consultation with Watts, Ericson answered as best he could: they had located the trouble, and would almost certainly be

191

able to clear it, but it would probably take them most of the night to do it.

Viperous, who had stopped her swift approach as soon as she was in effective touch, circled lazily about ten miles off them while the signals were exchanged. Then there was a pause and then she signalled: 'Afraid I cannot spare you an escort for the night.'

'That is quite all right,' Ericson signalled back. 'We will sleep by ourselves.' He put that in, in case *Viperous* were feeling sad about the arrangement. It was perfectly true that two escorts could not be spared from the convoy during the night; there could be no argument about the rightness of that decision.

There was another pause. *Viperous* began to shape up towards the northward horizon again. When she was stern-on to them:

'I must leave you to it,' she signalled finally. 'Best of luck.' She began to draw away. Just before she got out of touch she signalled again: 'Goodnight, Cinderella.'

' "Goodnight, dear elder sister",' Ericson dictated to Rose. But then he cancelled the message, before Rose started sending. The captain of *Viperous* was just a little bit too elder – in rank – for him to run the risk.

The repairs did not take all the night, but they took many trying hours of it. Watts had to cut the oil pipe eight times before he found the exact point of obstruction: this was at the joint of the elbow, and consisted of a lump of cotton waste hardened and compressed into a solid plug. The question of how it got there gave Watts half an hour of abusive and infuriated speculation and left Leading Stoker Gracey, along with the rest of the engine room complement, in sullen contemplation of the whole system of naval discipline. But time was not there to be wasted: even as he raged and questioned, Watts was working swiftly on the pieces of piping, brazing them together again into something like the same length and curve as they had had before. The result did not look very reassuring, and once they were delayed and very nearly defeated by a section which succumbed to the heat of the blow lamp and collapsed into solid metal: but finally the whole pipe was cleared and smoothed off, and they set to work to coax it back into position again.

Outside, dusk had come down, and then the night. With its coming, they took extraordinary precautions against discovery: Lockhart went round the upper deck three or four times to ensure that the ship was properly darkened and that no chink of light would betray them: the radios in the wardroom and the messdecks were closed down, and stringent orders given against unnecessary noise, and the lashings of the rafts cast off – in case, as Tallow put it morbidly, they had to make a rush job of swimming. 'And if any of you,' he added to the hands working on the upper deck, 'makes a noise tonight, I'll have his guts for a necktie. . . .' Their situation now involved a worse risk than any stopping or loitering had done before, because this time they were quite helpless: if a torpedo passed right underneath them, they could only wave goodbye to it, and wait for the next one. As the hours passed, the tension became unbearable: this was the sea, the very stretch of water which on their outward voyage had seen so many men go to their death, and here they were, sitting on it like a paralysed duck and waiting for the bang.

But there was nothing to do but wait. Watch succeeded watch: the hands tiptoed delicately to their stations, instead of clumping along the deck or stamping their sea boots on the iron ladders, as they usually did: *Compass Rose* floated motionless, with the black water occasionally slapping against her side: a brilliant quarter moon hung in the mid-Atlantic sky, showing them all the outlines of their hazard. Throughout the ship there was the same tension, the same disbelief in the future, the same rage against the bloody stokers down below who had let the engine get gummed up, and were now loafing and fiddling about. . . . Lockhart had it in mind to give the watch on deck, and the other spare hands, something definite to do, to take their attention away from the present danger; but everything he thought of – such as fire drill or lowering a boat to the water line – involved noise and probably the flashing of torches on the upper deck, and in the end he abandoned the idea and left them alone. Waiting in idleness was bad for the nerves; but the risk attending anything else might be worse still.

Ericson spent all these hours up on the bridge: there was no other station for him at such a moment, and no other choice in his mind. The lookouts changed half-hourly: cocoa came up in relays from the wardroom: the asdic and the radar kept up their incessant watch: curbing his immense impatience, Ericson sat on, enthroned like some wretched ragamuffin chief on the bridge of his useless ship. Mostly he stared at the water and the horizon, sometimes at the bright moon which no cloud would obscure: occasionally he watched the shadowy figures on the upper deck, the men who waited there in silent groups, collected round the guns or the boats, instead of going below and turning in. This was a new thing aboard *Compass Rose*. But he could not find fault with their prudence, he could not blame them for their fear.

There was an example of this nervous strain much closer at hand. Ferraby had not been below decks since the ship came to a stop, and now he was curled up in a blanket at the side of the bridge: he lay on his back, his hands clasped behind his head, his inflated lifejacket ballooning out like some opulent bosom; he had been there since he came off watch, at midnight, and he had never stirred or changed his position. Ericson had thought that he was dozing; but once, taking a turn round the bridge, he had noticed that the other man's eyes were wide open, and that he was darkly staring at the sky overhead. There was a sheen of perspiration at his temples. He was very far from sleep. . . . Ericson paused in his pacing, and looked down at the pale face.

'All right, Sub?' he asked conversationally.

There was no answer, and no sign that he had been heard. But Ericson did not persist with his question: this was a time to disregard people's reactions, to look past them without comment. The ship had been stopped, a still and defenceless target, for over twelve hours: *Sorrel* was fresh in all their minds: this was where it had all happened before. It was no wonder that, here and there, nerves stretched to breaking-point were

194

jumping and quivering in the effort to hold on.

He walked to the front of the bridge again, and sat down without another word. Ferraby could not help what was happening to him: no blame attached to him for his raw nerves, any more than a new-born child could be blamed for weighing six pounds instead of eight. The womb of war had produced him thus. But somewhere at the back of his mind Ericson was conscious of a strange sort of envy, an irritated consciousness of what a huge relief it would be to relax his grip, to surrender the unmoving mask of competence, to show to the world, if need be, his fatigue or fear. . . . Gibraltar, he thought suddenly: I gave up there, Lockhart saw it – but that had been alcohol, alcohol and guilt, nothing else. And it was not to happen again, it was not to happen now. . . . Waiting in the darkness, watching the silver ripples crossing the track of the moon, he slowly tightened up again.

Only once during that night was there an interruption of their vigil, but it was an interruption which startled them all. In the stillness that followed the change of the watch, just after midnight, breaking harshly in upon the sound of lapping water, there was a sudden burst of hammering from below, a solid succession of thuds which resounded throughout the ship. Everyone came to attention, and looked at his neighbour in quest of reassurance: secretly they cursed the men working in the engine room, for reawakening their fear and their hatred. The noise could be heard for miles around. . . . On the bridge, Ericson turned to Morell, who had just taken over the watch.

'Go down and see Watts,' he said crisply. 'Tell him to stop the hammering or to muffle it somehow. Tell him we can't afford to make this amount of noise.' As Morell turned to go, Ericson added, less formally, 'Tell him the torpedo will hit him first.'

That was perfectly true, thought Morell, as he climbed down successive ladders deep into the heart of the ship: to go below the waterline at a moment such as this was like stepping knowingly into the tomb. He could not help feeling a comradely admiration for the men who had been working patiently, ten feet below the surface of the water, for so many hours on end: it was part of their job, of course, just as it had sometimes been part of his own to be up on the exposed bridge when an aircraft was spraying them with machine-gun fire: but the coldblooded hazard involved in working below decks in the present circumstances seemed to demand a special category of nervous endurance. If a torpedo came, the engine-room crew must be an instant casualty: they would have perhaps ten seconds to get out, as the water flooded in, and those ten seconds, for a dozen men fighting to use one ladder in the pitch darkness, would mean the worst end to life that a man could devise. . . . But hazard or not, they oughtn't to make so much noise about what they were doing: that was stretching their necks out too far altogether.

The hammering stopped as he slid down the last oily ladder to the engine room itself, and Watts, hearing his step on the iron plating, turned to greet him.

'Come to see the fun, sir? It won't be long now.'

'That's my idea of good news, Chief,' answered Morell. No settled naval hierarchy could ever make him address Watts, who was nearly old enough to be his grandfather, with anything save an informal friendliness. 'But the Captain's a bit worried about the noise. Can you do anything to tone it down?'

'Pretty well finished now, sir,' said Watts. 'We were just putting one of those brackets back. . . . Could you hear the hammering up top?'

'Hear it? There were submarines popping up for miles around, complaining about the racket.'

There was a short laugh from the handful of men working round the oil pipe: down there, even the funniest jokes about submarines were only just funny. . . . Morell looked round the circle of faces, harshly lit by the naked hand lamp clipped to a nearby stanchion: they all shared the same look, the same factors of expression – tiredness, concentration, fear in the background. He knew them all by sight – Watts, Leading Stoker Gracey, a couple of young second-class stokers named Binns and Spurway who were always getting drunk ashore, an apprentice ERA called Broughton who was a Roman Catholic – but he had never known them quite like this: the labels and the characters he usually attached to them seemed to have been stripped and melted away, leaving only the basic men whose brains and fingers either could or could not patch up the oil pipe before a submarine caught them, and whose faces reflected this uncertain future. There was no pettiness about them now, no individual foible, no trace of indiscipline: as they worked, Care sat on their shoulders, Time's winged chariot was at their backs (Morell smiled as the odd phrases, incongruous in the glare and smell of the engine room, returned to him), and they knew this all the time and it had purged them of everything save a driving anxiety to finish what they had to do.

'Any signs of submarines, sir?' asked Gracey after a pause. He was a Lancashire man: he pronounced the hated word as "soobmarines", giving it a humorous air which robbed it of its sting. Said like that, it was hardly a submarine at all, just something out of a musichall, no more lethal than a mother-in-law or a dish of tripe. How nice, thought Morell, if that were true.

'Nothing so far,' he answered. 'The convoy seems to be quite happy, too. But I don't think we want to hang about here too long.'

Watts nodded. 'Seems like we're sitting up and asking for it,' he said grimly. 'If they don't get us now, they never will.'

'How much longer, Chief?'

'Couple of hours, maybe.'

'Longest job we've ever had,' said Gracey. 'You'd think it was a bloody battle wagon.'

'Me for barracks, when we get in,' said Broughton, 'I'd rather run the boiler house at Chatham than this lot.'

'Who wouldn't?' said Spurway, the smallest and usually the drunkest stoker. '*I'd* rather clean out the dockside heads, any day of the week.'

Morell suddenly realized how intensely nervous thay had all become, how far they had been driven beyond the normal margins of behaviour. He said: 'Good luck with it,' and started up the ladder again. At the top, the stars greeted him, and then the black water. A small chill wind was stirring, sending quick ripples slapping against their side. Alone in the dark night, *Compass Rose* lay still, waiting.

In the cold hour that stretched between 2 and 3 a.m., with the moon clouded, and the water black and fathomless as sable, a step on the bridge ladder. But now it was a different sort of step: cheerful, quick-mounting, no longer stealthy. It was Chief ERA Watts.

'Captain, sir!' he called to the vague figure hunched over the front of the bridge.

Ericson, stiff and cold with his long vigil, turned awkwardly towards him. 'Yes, Chief?'

'Ready to move, sir.'

So that was that, thought Ericson, standing up and stretching gratefully: they could get going, they could leave at last this hated corner, they could make their escape. The relief was enormous, flooding in till it seemed to reach every part of his body: he felt like shouting his congratulations, seizing Watts's hand and shaking it, giving way to his light-headed happiness. But all he said was: 'Thank you, Chief. Very well done.' And then, to the voice pipe: 'Wheelhouse!'

'Wheelhouse, bridge, sir!' came the quartermaster's voice, startled from some dream of home.

'Ring "Stand by, main engines".'

Very soon they were off: steaming swiftly northwards, chasing the convoy: the revolutions mounted, the whole ship grew warm and alive and full of hope again. There was no need to look back: they had, by all the luck in the world, left nothing of themselves behind and given nothing to the enemy.

Rio Grande

There lies a ship at her moorings out there on yonder stream;
Her lines upon the water are lovely like a dream,
And like a dream she'll slip away with the first dawning gleam,
    For she's bound for Rio Grande with the morning tide.
Yes, she's bound for Rio Grande, and it's there that I would be,
And every rope aboard of her is singing to be free;
Oh, goodbye to your sweetheart dear and goodbye to your bride
If you're bound for Rio Grande with the morning tide!

I heard the seagulls piping round, and all they seemed to say
Was, 'Come you out, young sailorman, it's time to come away.
Oh, heave your donkey's breakfast in, there isn't time to stay
    If you're bound for Rio Grande with the morning tide –
If you're bound for Rio Grande away, and oceans two or three,
And ports a plenty up and down for likely lads to see,
All across the seas, Johnnie, round the world so wide
Going out to Rio Grande with the morning tide.'

The lights in Paddy Ryan's bar they're shining on the shore;
Bid your friends goodbye, Johnnie, pay you now your score,
For you don't want the sight or smell o' the harbour any more,
    When you're bound for Rio Grande with the morning tide.
And 'away my rolling river' – for the sun's put out the stars
A tangle in her royal yards, and the frost is on her spars;
Oh, the deep sea hunger's hold of her, and not to be denied,
Going out to Rio Grande with the morning tide!

IAN DEAR

How the *America* Won Her Cup

(From *The America's Cup*)

The 'auld mug', as Sir Thomas Lipton, one of the most persistent of the many British challengers who has tried to retrieve the America's Cup, called it, provides, in my opinion, the most exciting challenge in sailing today. Yet, despite the millions and millions of pounds spent in trying to wrest it from the Americans, it is still firmly bolted to its plinth in the New York Yacht Club. And it has been in American hands ever since it was first won by them way back in 1851. (The fact that the Americans say they will replace the cup in its case with the head of the man who loses it might be considered to act as an incentive towards its defence!) I was vice-president of the Committee of British Industry 1500 Club which raised funds for the last British challenge in 1980, and I must say the cost of making such a challenge appals me. But I'd love to have a crack at getting the Cup back and if someone gave me £2 million I'd have a go! Such a consistently successful defence of a trophy is unparalleled in sport, and I find the story of the original race, related below, fascinating. Under the modern rating rules, the America would not have won the famous race in 1851, and we would never have had this great challenge.

The Squadron's standard trophy for this race, to take place on the 22 August, was an 'ordinary' cup, worth 100 guineas, and Stevens proposed to race for it. The squadron immediately agreed, and agreed, too, at the American's request to waive the rule that yachts were not allowed to 'boom out', as the extreme rake of *America*'s masts made it essential that she be allowed to do so. The Squadron also accepted that the American yacht could withdraw if the wind did not exceed 6 knots, and the fact of her ownership by a syndicate, which would normally have barred her from racing in a squadron regatta. (The Royal Victoria at Ryde had already barred her for this reason.) In fact, *America* raced on her own terms. By this time the reputation of the American yacht had spread far and wide and both the gentry and ordinary folk flocked to the island to watch the race. *The Times* commented:

In the memory of man Cowes never presented such an appearance as upon last Friday. There must have been upwards of 100 yachts lying at anchor in the Roads, the beach was crowded from Egypt [Point?] to the piers, the Esplanade in front of the club thronged with gentlemen and ladies, and the people inland who came over in shoals with wives, sons and daughters for the day. Booths were erected all along the quay, and the roadstead was alive with boats, while from the sea and shore rose an incessant buzz of voices, mingled with the splashing of oars, the flapping of sails, and the hissing of steam from the excursion vessels preparing to accompany the race.

Not all that unlike Newport on a similar occasion perhaps.

Quite unlike Newport, however, and the efficiency of the modern race committee of the NYYC, *The Times* correspondent goes on to mention that the cards with the names and colours of the participating yachts described the course as merely being 'round the Isle of Wight', while the printed programme stated that it was to be 'round the Isle of Wight, inside No-man's buoy and Sandhead buoy, and outside the Nab'. In short, there were two sets of racing instructions!

Eighteen yachts entered the race but three dropped out. The remaining fifteen were moored in a double line, 300 yards apart. One row consisted of cutters, the other of seven schooners. It was to be an open race with no time allowances. A preparatory gun was fired at 09.55. Despite the reporter for the *Illustrated London News* recording that *America* hoisted her new jib 'with all alacrity', the visitor was last away. Colonel Hamilton stated in his reminiscences that Stevens gave orders that the sails were not to be hoisted until all the other competitors had got under way. But the most likely explanation of the delay is described by an eyewitness on board, George Steers's younger nephew Henry, when he described the start some years later:

The first gun was to prepare, and then you could get up your sails – that is the schooners could hoist their fore and mainsails and the cutters their mainsails. Well, we attempted to hoist ours, and, the wind being to westward, we overran our anchor, and kept slewing around, so we had to lower them again.

Whatever the reason for her tardiness the American yacht was soon in pursuit of the others. *Gipsey Queen* led with *Beatrice* second, and all the way out to No-man's buoy the positions of the yachts changed as the wind increased and then died away. At one point a West India mail steamer got near enough to the yachts to cause an uncomfortable chop, reminding the modern reader that even during this, the first America's Cup race, the competitors were plagued as they have been ever since by spectators. The motion rendered some people aboard the various craft following the race 'ghastly looking and uncomfortable', according to *The Times,* which also recorded that at No-man's buoy only two minutes separated *America* from the leader *Volante,* and she lay fifth. Three others followed close behind while the rest, as *The Times* put it, staggered about in the rear. Soon afterwards one of them, *Wyvern,* returned to Cowes. *The Times* does not record how *America* managed to run through the rest of the fleet but several other sources – all American – make it clear that the American yacht was not always given free water as she gradually forged her way to the front.

In a pamphlet, 'A Chapter in the History of the Queen's Cup', issued by a Mr W. W. Evans in 1885, in answer to some 'snarlings' on the part of the *Saturday Review* as to the honesty of American yachtsmen, Evans states that 'more than a quarter of a century ago' (i.e. nine years after the race) a relation of his, a Mr John Rutherford, who had been on *America* during the race, told him:

Com. Stevens was standing on the quarter deck talking to a member of the Royal Yacht Squadron, that he carried in compliance with the rules. Chas Brown the sailing master, a New York pilot, was steering. In short time, and when near the No-Man's buoy, the *America* overhauled a large yacht. Brown attempted to pass her to windward, but the course of the yacht was changed and the *America* was headed off. Brown then attempted to pass to leeward, and was again headed off. He then, exasperated by this foul treatment, said to Mr Stevens, 'Commodore, shall I put the bow-sprit in the back of that fellow?'

Stevens said, 'No don't do it,' and turning to the member of the Royal Yacht Squadron, a Captain in the Royal Navy, said, 'Captain L, you may call this fair-play on this side of the ocean, but we, on the other side, would call it ——— foul play.'

The Captain remained mute, what could he say? His blood was probably boiling to think that any of his countrymen would attempt a dirty trick on a grand occasion when the eyes of all the yachting world were upon them.

Not the last time a club representative was to feel uneasy at the tactics of his own side!

The rest of the pamphlet does not lead one to believe particularly in the accuracy of Evans's reporting, which is hearsay anyway – but Henry Steers and another American source mention similar incidents. Whatever the difficulties the Americans may have had in establishing a lead, by 11.30 they had done so.

On board *America* was an experienced local pilot called Underwood to guide her who'd been engaged by the American consul at Portsmouth. As warnings had come from several quarters not to trust anybody to pilot the yacht in such treacherous waters, Stevens was very glad to receive someone who proved to be entirely reliable. Even so, according to Hamilton, Stevens received dire warnings. 'So strong was the distrust among our countrymen outside,' said Hamilton, 'that, even after the pilot was in charge, the commodore was warned by letter not to trust too much to him and urged to take another pilot to overlook him. . . . No one now can realize the anxieties of that contest, for we knew the ground was most unfavourable for us.' The pressure of international competition is obviously not a modern phenomenon.

Underwood opted, naturally, for the inner course. Four of the others, however, *Arrow*, *Bacchante*, *Constance* and *Gipsey Queen*, obeyed the other set of instructions and stood away to pass round the Nab, which, as *The Times* pointed out, was certainly the normal course to take. The rest of the fleet followed the inside course. The wind freshened and *America* opened up her lead despite being rather slow in stays when tacking. Then, at 12.58, another incident occurred which was to be repeated time and again during Cup races over the next century or so: one of *America's* spars – her jib boom – broke, and away went her flying jib. The skipper, who never had liked using this particular sail when working to windward, just said he was damned glad it was gone but the yacht was delayed by about a quarter of an hour while the wreckage was cleared. As it happened the breakage did not cost the syndicate a penny as Steers had got Ratsey, who had supplied the boom, to bet the cost of it that *Beatrice* would win the race, and the sailmaker to bet the cost of the sail that *America* would lose. The Americans must have been delighted that the cautious Britons had summoned enough sporting spirit to bet something on their ability or lack of it.

The incident did no great harm as her competitors by this time were miles astern – even the small tonnage cutters, *Aurora*, *Freak* and *Volante*, which could have been expected to have some advantage because of the light winds and greater manoeuvrability.

The next incident came at three o'clock when *Arrow* managed to run herself on the rocks. *Alarm* went to her assistance. At this point the wind freshened again and so great was the American yacht's apparent superiority that many of her competitors turned for home. However, three, *Aurora*, *Freak* and *Volante*, hung on, keeping close company as they hugged the coast to avoid the adverse tide while their American adversary stood right off from it. Alas, they kept too close together for *Freak* fouled *Volante* and the latter was forced to retire with her bowsprit carried away, and by 5.40, with *America* close to the Needles, *Aurora* was apparently nearly eight miles astern with *Freak* a further mile astern of her. The others were hardly in sight. Meanwhile, the royal yacht with the Queen and the Prince Regent on board appeared off the Needles before turning and laying off Alum Bay. Lord Alfred Paget, in the royal yacht's tender, *Fairy,* was sent off round the Needles to see who was in sight while the royal party landed and went for a stroll. They did not stay long however because a wet drizzle drifted in with the wind, which was now blowing faintly from the west-south-west. Lord Paget returned, reported on the position of the American yacht, and was sent off again to see if he could spot any of the others.

The famous exchange of the Queen having been told who was first, asking who was second and being given the reply, after a pregnant pause, that there was no second, must have occurred, if it occurred at all, when Paget returned the second time. It is impossible to know now whether this exchange did occur, but with the wind now light and with only the last of the flood to help her *America* took nearly three more hours to reach the finishing line off Cowes at 8.37, having rounded the Needles at 5.50. Yet *Aurora,* reported seven or eight miles astern before *America* reached the Needles, came in only a matter of minutes later. Certainly, by this time, the weather had deteriorated and this could have made it difficult to identify the yachts. The *Morning Post* described the scene graphically; reading its report now it is easy to understand how confusion could indeed have occurred.

A cutter called the *Wildfire* ran out from Sandown bay ahead of the *America,* and taking advantage of her favourable position, for some time kept ahead. She carried a colour similar to that of the *Aurora,* and caused a great confusion, as she was mistaken for that vessel.

There was enough going on at the time – with *America* sailing through the large spectator fleet at the Needles and then along-side the royal yacht and raising their hats and cheering and doing all sorts of unrepublican, not to say unseamanlike, actions (considering they were in the middle of a race) – for mistakes in identification to be made. It is certainly difficult to see how such a great distance could have been made up by

Aurora in such a comparatively short time. On the other hand there seems to be no consensus of opinion as to when *Aurora* finished. One report denies that any yacht came in at all, saying that fireworks were being displayed and it was dark. Stevens himself merely said, 'I could not learn correctly at what time, and in what order, the others arrived,' while the *Illustrated London News* stated that *Aurora* arrived 21 minutes later, and others said 24. But the New York Yacht Club eventually accepted 8 minutes as being correct, and this is what *The Times* said too. *Aurora* has really never been given sufficient credit for her performance but probably if the course had been but a few miles longer the greatest yachting trophy in the world would never have left British shores.

EDWARD LEAR

The Jumblies

This poem by Edward Lear always recalls for me my first long voyage in
Suhaili *in 1965. We were halfway between Bombay and Muscat when
we developed a very serious leak which kept the three of us on board bailing
solidly for thirty hours until the sea went down and we were able to get
overside and caulk the hull. During a quick rest between bailing, my
brother Chris, slumped on one of the bunks, suddenly started to recite this:*

I

They went to sea in a Sieve, they did,
  In a Sieve they went to sea:
In spite of all their friends could say,
On a winter's morn, on a stormy day,
  In a Sieve they went to sea!
And when the Sieve turned round and round,
And every one cried, 'You'll all be drowned!'
They called aloud, 'Our Sieve ain't big,
But we don't care a button! we don't care a fig!
  In a Sieve we'll go to sea!'
    Far and few, far and few,
      Are the lands where the Jumblies live;
      Their heads are green, and their hands are blue,
        And they went to sea in a Sieve.

II

They sailed away in a Sieve, they did,
  In a Sieve they sailed so fast

207

With only a beautiful pea-green veil
Tied with a riband by way of a sail,
 To a small tobacco-pipe mast;
And every one said, who saw them go,
'O won't they be soon upset, you know!
For the sky is dark, and the voyage is long,
And happen what may, it's extremely wrong
 In a Sieve to sail so fast!'
  Far and few, far and few,
   Are the lands where the Jumblies live;
    Their heads are green, and their hands are blue,
     And they went to sea in a Sieve.

III

The water it soon came in, it did,
 The water it soon came in;
So to keep them dry, they wrapped their feet
In a pinky paper all folded neat,
 And they fastened it down with a pin.
And they passed the night in a crockery-jar,
And each of them said, 'How wise we are!
Though the sky be dark, and the voyage be long,
Yet we never can think we were rash or wrong,
 While round in our Sieve we spin!'
  Far and few, far and few,
   Are the lands where the Jumblies live;
    Their heads are green, and their hands are blue,
     And they went to sea in a Sieve.

IV

And all night long they sailed away;
 And when the sun went down,
They whistled and warbled a moony song
To the echoing sound of a coppery gong,
 In the shade of the mountains brown.
'O Timballo! How happy we are,
When we live in a sieve and a crockery-jar,

208

And all night long in the moonlight pale,
We sail away with a pea-green sail,
   In the shade of the mountains brown!'
      Far and few, far and few,
        Are the lands where the Jumblies live;
       Their heads are green, and their hands are blue,
       And they went to sea in a Sieve.

V

They sailed to the Western Sea, they did,
   To a land all covered with trees,
And they bought an Owl, and a useful Cart,
And a pound of Rice, and a Cranberry Tart,
   And a hive of silvery Bees.
And they bought a Pig, and some green Jack-daws,
And a lovely Monkey with lollipop paws,
And forty bottles of Ring-Bo-Ree,
   And no end of Stilton Cheese.
      Far and few, far and few,
        Are the lands where the Jumblies live;
       Their heads are green, and their hands are blue,
       And they went to sea in a Sieve.

VI

And in twenty years they all came back,
   In twenty years or more,
And every one said, 'How tall they've grown!
For they've been to the Lakes, and the Torrible Zone,
   And the hills of the Chankly Bore';
And they drank their health, and gave them a feast
Of dumplings made of beautiful yeast;
And every one said, 'If we only live,
We too will go to sea in a Sieve, –
   To the hills of the Chankly Bore!'
      Far and few, far and few,
        Are the lands where the Jumblies live;
       Their heads are green, and their hands are blue,
       And they went to sea in a Sieve.

DAVID LEWIS

Antarctic Capsize

(From *Ice Bird*)

David Lewis, a New Zealander by birth, is, I believe, one of the most remarkable yachtsmen alive today, and, luckily for us, he is one who can really write about his experiences in a way which makes them live for his reader. A doctor by profession he gave up full-time practice in 1964 to pursue his passion for the sea and adventure. He took part in the first two single-handed trans-Atlantic races and after the second one went on to complete the first circumnavigation in a multi-hull with his wife, two small daughters, and, for part of the way, a friend, as crew. But he is an explorer as well as a racing man and in 1963 he led the Greenland Sea Expedition, and in 1977–78 headed an eight-man expedition to Antarctica. He is the author of several books, one of which, We, The Navigators, *is based on sailing for nine months with the traditional star-path navigators in the South Pacific. But perhaps his most memorable adventure was when he attempted the first single-handed circumnavigation of Antarctica. He failed, after capsizing three times and being dismasted twice. But what a story, and how well he told it, as this extract from* Ice Bird *reveals.*

Barry and I had weathered Coral Sea cyclone 'Becky' in *Isbjorn*, only partially sheltered by an inadequate island. Severe gales off Iceland, Magellan Strait and the Cape of Good Hope had been ridden out by *Rehu Moana* – the most seaworthy catamaran built so far – in the course of her Iceland voyage and her circumnavigation.

But this storm was something altogether new. By evening the estimated wind speed was over sixty knots; the seas were conservatively forty feet high and growing taller – great hollow rollers, whose wind-torn crests thundered over and broke with awful violence. The air was thick with driving spray.

Ice Bird was running down wind on the starboard gybe (the wind on the starboard quarter), with storm jib sheeted flat as before. Once again I adjusted the wind vane to hold the yacht steering at a small angle to a dead run, and laid out the tiller lines where they could be grasped instantaneously to assist the vane. This strategy had served me well in the gale just past, as it had Dumas and Moitessier. But would it be effective against this fearful storm? Had any other precautions been neglected? The Beaufort inflatable liferaft's retaining strops had been reinforced by a criss-cross of extra lashings across the cockpit. Everything movable, I thought, was securely battened down; the washboards were snugly in place in the companionway; the hatches were all secured. No, I could not think of anything else that could usefully be done.

Came a roar, as of an approaching express train. Higher yet tilted the stern; *Ice Bird* picked up speed and hurtled forward surfing on her nose, then slewed violently to starboard, totally unresponsive to my hauling at the tiller lines with all my strength. A moment later the tottering breaker exploded right over us, smashing the yacht down onto her port side. The galley shelves tore loose from their fastenings and crashed down in a cascade of jars, mugs, frying pan and splintered wood. I have no recollection of where I myself was flung – presumably backwards onto the port bunk. I only recall clawing my way up the companionway and staring aft through the dome.

The invaluable self-steering vane had disappeared and I found, when I scrambled out on deck, that its vital gearing was shattered beyond repair – stainless-steel shafts twisted and cog wheels and worm gear gone altogether. The stout canvas dodger round the cockpit was hanging in tatters. The jib was torn, though I am not sure whether it had split right across from luff to clew then or later. My recollections are too confused and most of that day's log entries were subsequently destroyed.

I do know that I lowered the sail, slackening the halyard, hauling down the jib and securing it, repeatedly unseated from the jerking foredeck, half blinded by stinging spray and sleet, having to turn away my head to gulp for the air being sucked past me by the screaming wind. Then lying on my stomach and grasping handholds like a rock climber, I inched my way back to the companionway and thankfully pulled the hatch to after me.

I crouched forward on the edge of the starboard bunk doing my best to persuade *Ice Bird* to run off before the wind under bare poles. She answered the helm, at best erratically, possibly because she was virtually becalmed in the deep canyons between the waves; so that more often than not the little yacht wallowed broadside on, port beam to the sea, while I struggled with the tiller lines, trying vainly to achieve steerage way and control.

And still the wind kept on increasing. It rose until, for the first time in all my years of seagoing, I heard the awful high scream of force 13 hurricane winds rising beyond 70 knots.

The remains of the already shredded canvas dodger streamed out horizontally, flogging with so intense a vibration that the outlines blurred. Then the two stainless-steel wires supporting the dodger parted and in a flash it was gone. The whole sea was white now. Sheets of foam, acres in extent, were continually being churned anew by fresh cataracts. These are not seas, I thought: they are the Snowy Mountains of Australia – and they are rolling right over me. I was very much afraid.

Some time later – I had no idea how long – my terror receded into some remote corner of my mind. I must have shrunk from a reality I could no longer face into a world of happier memories, for I began living in the past again, just as I had in my exhaustion in the gale two days earlier. It is hard to explain the sensation. I did not move over from a present world into an illusory one but temporarily inhabited both at once and was fully aware of doing so, without feeling this to be in any way strange or alarming. My handling of the tiller was quite automatic.

Mounts Kosciusko, Townsend, the broken crest of Jagungal; sculptured summits, sweeping snow slopes streaked with naked rock; all this mighty snow panorama rolled past like a cinema film. It was moving because those snow mountains were simultaneously the too-fearful-to-contemplate water mountains of paralysing reality.

I am watching, as from afar, four of us gliding down off the snow-plumed divide, four dots in a vast whiteness. Then I am striving for balance under the weight of my pack, skis rattling a bone-shaking tattoo over a serration of ice ridges. We ski to a rest under a snow cornice overlooking the headwaters of the Snowy River, where we tunnel a snow cave to shelter us for the night – a survival exercise in preparation for my present venture.

But why are those snow mountains rolling onward? Where are they going? I have drifted away even further from the present and my tired brain baulks at the effort of solving the conundrum.

The picture blurs. I am leading a party up this same Kosciusko during the winter lately past, something like three months ago, amid the same rounded shoulders and rolling summits – literally rolling. My little Susie, refusing help with her pack, plods gamely up the endless snow slope, eyes suffused with tears of tiredness. We halt to rest. Almost at once, with the resilience of childhood, Susie is away – laughing, her tears forgotten, the swish of her skis answering the song of the keen mountain wind.

The intolerable present became too intrusive to be ignored; the past faded into the background. Veritable cascades of white water were now thundering past on either side, more like breakers monstrously enlarged to perhaps forty-five feet, crashing down on a surf beach. Sooner or later one must burst fairly over us. What then?

I wedged myself more securely on the lee bunk, clutching the tiller lines, my stomach hollow with fear. The short sub-Antarctic night was over; it was now about 2 a.m.

My heart stopped. My whole world reared up, plucked by an irresistible force, to spin through giddy darkness, then to smash

213

down into daylight again. Daylight, I saw with horror, as I pushed aside the cabin table that had come down on my head (the ceiling insulation was scored deeply where it had struck the deck head) . . . daylight was streaming through the now gaping opening where the forehatch had been! Water slopped about my knees. The remains of the Tilly lamp hung askew above my head. The stove remained upside down, wedged in its twisted gymballs.

Ice Bird had been rolled completely over to starboard through a full 360° and had righted herself thanks to her heavy lead keel – all in about a second. In that one second the snug cabin had become a shambles. What of the really vital structures? Above all, what of the mast?

I splashed forward, the first thought in my mind to close that yawning fore hatchway. My second – oh, God – the mast. I stumbled over rolling cans, felt the parallel rules crunch underfoot and pushed aside the flotsam of clothes, mattresses, sleeping bag, splintered wood fragments and charts (British charts floated better than Chilean, I noted – one up to the Admiralty). Sure enough the lower seven feet of the mast, broken free of the mast step, leaned drunkenly over the starboard bow and the top twenty-nine feet tilted steeply across the ruptured guard wires and far down into the water, pounding and screeching as the hulk wallowed.

The forehatch had been wrenched open by a shroud as the mast fell. Its hinges had sprung, though they were not broken off and its wooden securing batten had snapped. I forced it as nearly closed as I could with the bent hinges and bowsed it down with the block and tackle from the bosun's chair.

Then I stumbled back aft to observe, incredulously, for the first time that eight feet of the starboard side of the raised cabin trunk had been dented in, longitudinally, as if by a steam hammer. A six-inch vertical split between the windows spurted water at every roll (it was noteworthy, and in keeping with the experience of others, that it had been the lee or downwind side, the side underneath as the boat capsized, that had sustained damage, not the weather side where the wave had struck).

What unimaginable force could have done that to eighth-inch steel? The answer was plain. Water. The breaking crest, which had picked up the seven-ton yacht like a matchbox, would have been hurtling forward at something like fifty miles an hour. When it slammed her over, the impact would have been equivalent to dumping her onto concrete. The underside had given way.

Everything had changed in that moment of capsize on 29 November at 60°04′ S, 135°35′ W, six weeks and 3600 miles out from Sydney, 2500 miles from the Antarctic Peninsula. Not only were things changed; everything was probably coming to an end. The proud yacht of a moment before had become a wreck: high adventure had given place to an apparently foredoomed struggle to survive.

ANTHONY HECKSTALL-SMITH

Willie Fife

(From *Sacred Cowes*)

One of my favourite places on the Clyde was William Fife's yard at Fairlie, and old Willie Fife was one of my favourite people. A bachelor, who sometimes hid his shyness behind a dour Scottish manner, he had a robust sense of humour that often caused him to weep with laughter at the behaviour of some of his clients who had more money than sea-sense.

Like all great artists, and there was none greater than he, Willie could be autocratic. Once, a rich newcomer to the sport called at Fairlie to order not one but two 12-metres.

'Can you guarantee they'll be fast, Mr Fife?' he asked, bringing out his cheque book.

Fife took off the rusty old bowler he always wore in the yard, and scratched his bald head.

'Can you guarantee to sail them?' he asked.

NEIL MUNRO

Treasure Trove

(From *Para Handy Tales*)

Most people have heard of Para Handy and his crew and the Clyde Puffer the Vital Spark, *created by Neil Munro, and many will remember the delightful film series based on his book,* Para Handy Tales, *from which this story is taken. But what many people perhaps don't realize, unless they cruise round the Western Isles of Scotland, is how true Para Handy's attitudes still are today. A chap can still say he'll be back in ten minutes and it can still be three days before he turns up again! And the people are absolutely charming but they'll pull a fast one if they possibly can, which is what this piece is all about.*

Sunny Jim proved a most valuable acquisition to the *Vital Spark*. He was a person of humour and resource, and though they were sometimes the victims of his practical jokes, the others of the crew forgave him readily because of the fun he made. It is true that when they were getting the greatest entertainment from him they were, without thinking it, generally doing his work for him – for indeed he was no sailor, only a Clutha mariner – but at least he was better value for his wages than The Tar, who could neither take his fair share of the work nor tell a baur. Sunny Jim's finest gift was imagination; the most wonderful things in the world had happened to him when he was on the Clutha – all intensely interesting, if incredible: and Para Handy, looking at him with admiration and even envy, after a narrative more extraordinary than usual, would remark, 'Man! it's a peety

217

listenin' to such d—d lies iss a sin, for there iss no doubt it iss a most pleasant amuusement!'

Macphail the engineer, the misanthrope, could not stand the new hand. 'He's no' a sailor at a'!' he protested; 'he's a clown; I've see'd better men jumpin' through girrs at a penny show.'

'Weel, he's maybe no' awful steady at the wheel, but he hass a kyind, kyind he'rt!' Dougie said.

'He's chust sublime!' said Para Handy. 'If he wass managed right there would be money in him!'

Para Handy's conviction that there was money to be made out of Sunny Jim was confirmed by an episode at Tobermory, of which the memory will be redolent in Mull for years to come.

The *Vital Spark,* having discharged a cargo of coal at Oban, went up the Sound to load with timber, and on Calve Island, which forms a natural breakwater for Tobermory harbour, Dougie spied a stranded whale. He was not very much of a whale as whales go in Greenland, being merely a tiny fellow of about five-and-twenty tons, but as dead whales here are as rarely to be seen as dead donkeys, the *Vital Spark* was steered close in to afford a better view, and even stopped for a while that Para Handy and his mate might land with the punt on the islet and examine the unfortunate cetacean.

'My Chove! he's a whupper!' was Dougie's comment, as he reached up and clapped the huge mountain of sea-flesh on its ponderous side. 'It wass right enough, I can see, Peter, aboot yon fellow Jonah; chust look at the accommodation!'

'Chust waste, pure waste,' said the skipper; 'you can make a meal off a herrin', but whales iss only lumber, goin' aboot ass big as a land o' hooses, blowin' aal the time, and puttin' the fear o' daith on aal the other fushes. I never had mich respect for them.'

'If they had a whale like that aground on Clyde,' said Dougie, as they returned to the vessel, 'they would stick bills on't; it's chust thrown away on the Tobermory folk.'

Sunny Jim was enchanted when he heard the whale's dimensions. 'Chaps,' he said with enthusiasm, 'there's a fortune in't; right-oh! I've see'd them chargin' tuppence to get into a tent at

Vinegar Hill, whaur they had naethin' fancier nor a sealion or a seal.'

'But they wouldna be deid,' said Para Handy; 'and there's no' mich fun aboot a whale's remains. Even if there was, we couldna tow him up to Gleska, and if we could, he wouldna keep.'

'Jim'll be goin' to embalm him, rig up a mast on him, and sail him up the river; are ye no', Jim?' said Macphail with irony.

'I've a faur better idea than that,' said Sunny Jim. 'Whit's to hinder us clappin' them tarpaulins roon' the whale whaur it's lyin', and showin' 't at a sixpence a heid to the Tobermory folk? Man! ye'll see them rowin' across in hunners, for I'll bate ye there's no' much fun in Tobermory in the summertime unless it's a Band o' Hope soiree. Give it a fancy name – the "Tobermory Treasure"; send the bellman roond the toon, sayin' it's on view tomorrow from ten till five, and then goin' on to Oban; Dougie'll lift the money, and the skipper and me'll tell the audience a' aboot the customs o' the whale when he's in life. Macphail can stand by the ship at Tobermory quay.'

'Jist what I said a' alang,' remarked Macphail darkly. 'Jumpin' through girrs! Ye'll need a big drum and a naphtha lamp.'

'Let us first paause and consider,' remarked Para Handy, with his usual caution; 'iss the whale oors?'

'Wha's else wad it be?' retorted Sunny Jim. 'It was us that fun' it, and naebody seen it afore us, for it's no' mony oors ashore.'

'Everything cast up on the shore belangs to the Crown; it's the King's whale,' said Macphail.

'Weel, let him come for 't,' said Sunny Jim; 'by the time he's here we'll be done wi't.'

The presumption that Tobermory could be interested in a dead whale proved quite right; it was the Glasgow Fair week, and the local boat-hirers did good business taking parties over to the island where an improvized enclosure of oars, spars, and tarpaulin and dry sails concealed the 'Tobermory Treasure' from all but those who were prepared to pay for admission. Para Handy, with his hands in his pockets and a studied air of indifference, as if the enterprise was none of his, chimed in at intervals with facts on the natural history of the whale, which Sunny Jim might overlook in the course of his introductory lecture.

'The biggest whale by three feet that's ever been seen in Scotland,' Sunny Jim announced. 'Lots o' folk thinks a whale's a fish, but it's naething o' the kind; it's a hot-blooded mammoth, and couldna live in the watter mair nor a wee while at a time withoot comin' up to draw its breath. This is no' yin of thae common whales that chases herrin', and goes pechin' up and doon Kilbrannan Sound; it's the kind that's catched wi' the harpoons and lives on naething but roary borealises and icebergs.'

'They used to make umbrella-rubs wi' this parteecular kind,' chimed in the skipper diffidently; 'forbye, they're full o' blubber. It's an aawful useful thing a whale, chentlemen.' He had apparently changed his mind about the animal, for which the previous day he had said he had no respect.

'Be shair and tell a' your friends when ye get ashore that it's maybe gaun on to Oban tomorrow,' requested Sunny Jim. 'We'll hae it up on the Esplanade there and chairge a shillin' a heid; if we get it the length o' Gleska, the price'll be up to hauf-a-croon.'

'Is it a "right" whale?' asked one of the audience in the interests of exact science.

'Right enough, as shair's onything; isn't it, Captain?' said Sunny Jim.

'What else would it be?' said Para Handy indignantly. 'Does the chentleman think there iss onything wrong with it? Perhaps he would like to take a look through it; eh, Jum? Or maybe he would want a doctor's certeeficate that it's no' a dromedary.'

The exhibition of the 'Tobermory Treasure' proved so popular that its discoverers determined to run their entertainment for about a week. On the third day passengers coming into Tobermory with the steamer *Claymore* sniffed with appreciation, and talked about the beneficial influence of ozone; the English tourists debated whether it was due to peat or heather.

In the afternoon several yachts in the bay hurriedly got up their anchors and went up Loch Sunart, where the air seemed fresher. On the fourth day the residents of Tobermory overwhelmed the local chemist with demands for camphor, carbolic powder, permanganate of potash, and other deodorants and disinfectants; and several plumbers were telegraphed for to Oban. The public patronage of the exhibition on Calve Island fell off.

'If there's ony mair o' them wantin' to see this whale,' said Sunny Jim, 'they'll hae to look slippy.'

'It's no' that bad to windward,' said Para Handy. 'What would you say to coverin' it up wi' more tarpaulins?'

'You might as weel cover't up wi' crape or muslin,' was Dougie's verdict. 'What you would need iss armour plate, the same ass they have roond the cannons in the man-o'-wars. If this wind doesn't change to the west, half the folk in Tobermory'll be goin' to live in the cellar o' the Mishnish Hotel.'

Suspicion fell on the 'Tobermory Treasure' on the following day, and an influential deputation waited on the police sergeant, while the crew of the *Vital Spark*, with much discretion, abandoned their whale, and kept to their vessel's fo'c'sle. The sergeant informed the deputation that he had a valuable clue to the source of these extraordinary odours, but that unfortunately he could take no steps without a warrant from the Sheriff, and the Sheriff was in Oban. The deputation pointed out that the circumstances were too serious to permit of any protracted legal forms and ceremonies; the whale must be removed from Calve Island by its owners immediately, otherwise there would be a plague. With regret the police sergeant repeated that he could do nothing without authority, but he added casually that if the deputation visited the owners of the whale and scared the life out of them, he would be the last man to interfere.

'Hullo, chaps! pull the hatch efter yez, and keep oot the cold air!' said Sunny Jim, as the spokesman of the deputation came seeking for the crew in the fo'c'sle. 'Ye'd be the better o' some odecolong on your hankies.'

'We thought you were going to remove your whale to Oban before this,' said the deputation sadly.

'I'm afraid,' said Para Handy, 'that whale hass seen its best days, and wouldna be at aal popular in Oban.'

'Well, you'll have to take it out of here immediately anyway,' said the deputation. 'It appears to be your property.'

'Not at aal, not at aal!' Para Handy assured him; 'it belongs by right to His Majesty, and we were chust takin' care of it for him till he would turn up, chairgin' a trifle for the use o' the tarpaulins and the management. It iss too great a responsibility now, and we've given up the job; aren't we, Jum?'

'Right-oh!' said Sunny Jim, reaching for his melodeon; 'and it's time you Tobermory folk were shiftin' that whale.'

'It's impossible,' said the deputation, 'a carcase weighing nearly thirty tons – and in such a condition!'

'Indeed it is pretty bad,' said Para Handy; 'perhaps it would be easier to shift the toon o' Tobermory.'

But that was, luckily, not necessary, as a high tide restored the 'Tobermory Treasure' to its natural element that very afternoon.

MICHAEL GREEN

A Coarse Sailor's Beaufort Scale

(From *The Art of Coarse Sailing*)

Specification of Beaufort Scale

	Description of wind	For Coarse use, based on observations made at Potter Heigham and Bosham	For use on land, based on observations made at land stations	Speed in nautical m.p.h.
0	Calm	Boat moves sideways with tide	Cigarette smoke gets in eyes	Less than 1
1	Light air	Coarse yachtsmen hoist sail, then wind instantly drops	Wet finger feels cold	1–3
2	Light breeze	Tea-towels blow off rigging	Public houses close one window	4–6
3	Gentle breeze	Coarse boats careen Difficult to make tea under way	Public houses close two windows	7–10
4	Moderate breeze	Gas keeps going out	Beer froth blows off	11–16
5	Fresh breeze	Coarse sailors get book on sailing from cabin and turn up bit on reefing	Customers in public-house gardens go inside bar	17–21
6	Strong breeze	Coarse sailors try to double reef and go aground	Elderly customers have difficulty in leaving public house	22–27

7	Moderate gale	Coarse sailors rescued by launch	Public-house door cannot be opened against wind	28–33
8	Fresh gale	Aaaaaaaaah ...	Public-house sign blows down	34–40
9	Strong gale	Coarse sailors in public house	Coarse sailors struck by falling sign	41–47

N.B. – Although the Beaufort Scale goes up to force 12 it is felt unlikely that anything over force 9 would interest coarse sailors except on a television programme.

CAPTAIN JOHN SMITH

Directions for Taking a Prize

(From *The Seaman's Grammar*)

For the romantic, the days of sail were full of stirring sea fights with handsome heroes, looking remarkably like Douglas Fairbanks Jr, swinging across a ship with a knife between their teeth, intent on plunder, a good fight and winning the heroine. All Hollywood scriptwriters' fiction of course. Except that the following piece was written about 1650 by Captain John Smith, who was at one time Governor of Virginia and Admiral of New England. It comes from a book entitled The Seaman's Grammar, *and is a very complete instruction of what to look for, and the actions and behaviour expected in a ship-to-ship battle. The reminder at the end as to how the defeated enemy should be treated is as appropriate today as it was 300 years ago.*

'A sail!' 'How bears she [*or* stands she]? To wind-ward or lee-ward? Set him by the compass!' 'He stands right-a-head [*or* on the weather-bow, *or* lee-bow].' 'Let fly your colours (if you have a consort, else not)! Out with all your sails! A steady man to the helm – sit close to keep her steady! Give him chase [*or* fetch him up]!' – 'He hold his own!' 'No – we gather on him, Captain!' Out goes his flag and pendants, also his waist-cloths and top-armings, which is a long red cloth about three-quarters of a yard broad, edged on each side with calico or white linen cloth, that goeth round about the ship on the outsides of all her upper works, fore and aft, and before the cubbridge-heads,[1] also

[1] The bulk-heads of the fore-castle.

about the fore- and main-tops, as well for the countenance and grace of the ship, as to cover the men from being seen. He furls and slings his main-yard; in goes his sprit-sail. Thus they use to strip themselves into their 'short sails', or 'fighting sails', which is, only the foresail, the main and fore top-sails, because the rest should not be fired nor spoiled; besides, they would be troublesome to handle, hinder our sights and the using our arms. He makes ready his close fights,[1] fore and aft.

'Master, how stands the chase?' 'Right on head, I say.' 'Well: we shall reach him bye and bye. What! is all ready?' 'Yea, yea.' 'Every man to his charge! Dowse your topsail to salute him for the sea: hail him with a noise of trumpets. Whence is your ship?' 'Of *Spain*: whence is yours?' 'Of *England*.' 'Are you a merchant, or a man-of-war?'[2] 'We are of the Sea!' He waves us to leeward with his drawn sword, calls amain for the king of Spain, and springs his luff.[3] 'Give him a chase-piece with your broad-side, and run a good berth a-head of him!' 'Done, done.' 'We have the wind of him, and he tacks about.' 'Tack you about also, and keep your luff![4] Be yare at the helm! Edge in with him! Give him a volley of small shot, also your prow and broad-side as before, and keep your luff.' 'He pays us shot for shot!' 'Well: we shall requite him!'

'What! Are you ready again?' 'Yea, yea!' 'Try him once more, as before!' 'Done, done!' 'Keep your luff and load your ordnance again: is all ready?' 'Yea, yea!' 'Edge in with him again! Begin with your bow-pieces, proceed with your broad-side, and let her fall off with the wind, to give her also your full chase, your weather broad-side, and bring her round that the stern may also discharge and your tacks close aboard again!' 'Done, done! ... The wind veers, the sea goes too high to board her, and we are shot thorough and thorough, and between wind and water.' 'Try the pump: bear up the helm! Master, let us breathe and refresh a little, and sling a man over-board to stop the leaks': that is to truss him up about the middle in a piece of canvas and

[1] Bulk-heads set up to cover the men while firing.
[2] Smith's original text has 'merchants, or men of war.'
[3] Brings his ship suddenly close by the wind.
[4] Keep nearer to the wind.

a rope to keep him from sinking, and his arms at liberty, with a mallet in the one hand, and a plug lapped in oakum, and well tarred, in a tarpawling clout in the other, which he will quickly beat into the hole or holes the bullets made. 'What cheer, mates? Is all well?' 'All well! – All well! – All well!' 'Then make ready to bear up with him again!' And with all your great and small shot charge him, and in the smoke board him thwart the hawse, on the bow, mid-ships, or, rather than fail, on his quarter; or make fast your grapplings, if you can, to his close fights, and sheer off. 'Captain, we are foul on each other, and the ship is on fire!' 'Cut anything to get clear, and smother the fire with wet cloths.' In such a case they will presently be such friends as to help one another all they can to get clear, lest they should both burn together and sink: and if they be generous, the fire quenched, drink kindly one to another, heave their cans over-board, and then begin again as before.

'Well, Master, the day is spent; the night draws on, let us consult. Chirurgeon, look to the wounded, and wind up the slain (with each a weight or bullet at their heads and feet to make them sink, and give them three guns for their funerals). Swabber, make clean the ship. Purser, record their names. Watch, be vigilant to keep your berth to windward, that we lose him not in the night. Gunners, spunge your ordnance. Soldiers, scour your pieces. Carpenters, about your leaks. Boatswain and the rest, repair the sails and shrouds, and Cook see you observe your directions against the morning watch.' . . . 'Boy, holla! Master, holla! is the kettle boiled?' 'Yea, yea!' 'Boatswain, call up the men to prayer and breakfast.'

'Boy, fetch my cellar of bottles. A health to you all, fore and aft! Courage, my hearts, for a fresh charge! Gunners, beat open the ports, and out with your lower tier, and bring me from the weather-side to the lee so many pieces as we have ports to bear upon him. Master, lay him aboard, luff for luff! Mid-ships men, see the tops and yards well manned, with stones, fire-pots, and brass balls, to throw amongst them before we enter: or if we be put off, charge them with all your great and small shot; in the smoke let us enter them in the shrouds, and every squadron at his best advantage. So, sound drums and trumpets, and SAINT GEORGE FOR ENGLAND!'

'They hang out a flag of truce!' 'Hail him amain, ABASE!'[1] (or take in his flag). They strike their sails, and come aboard with their captain, purser, and gunner, with their commission, cocket, or bills of loading. Out goes the boat: they are launched from the ship-side. Entertain them with a cry, 'God save the captain and all the company!' with the trumpets sounding. Examine them in particular, and then conclude your conditions, with feasting, freedom, or punishment, as you find occasion. But always have as much care to their wounded as to your own; and if there be either young women or aged men, use them nobly, which is ever the nature of a generous disposition. To conclude, if you surprise him, or enter perforce, you may stow the men, rifle, pillage, or sack, and cry a prize.

---

[1] I.e. 'Down with your flag!' The summons to surrender. Fr. *A bas!* Sp. *Abajo!*

NEIL HOLLANDER AND HARALD MERTES

An Alarm System for Grounding at Night

(From *The Yachtsman's Emergency Handbook*)

This idea for warning a yachtsman at night that he's about to ground appeals to me because it is simple and – provided the frying pan is sufficiently heavy! – pretty foolproof.

Drop a weight attached to a line over the side until it hangs 10–20 cm below the keel. ■ 111.

Run the line through a block to the cockpit or skylight where the end secures a pot or pan in place ■ 112.

When the weight touches ground, the line slackens and the pan crashes to the deck.

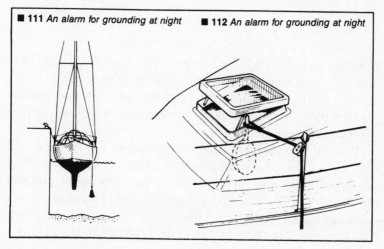

■ 111 *An alarm for grounding at night*   ■ 112 *An alarm for grounding at night*

DOUGLAS REEMAN

Air Attack

(From *Torpedo Run*)

I've always liked what's known as 'a rattling good yarn' and that prolific novelist of the sea, Douglas Reeman – he also writes under the name of Alexander Kent – spins them quite unlike anyone else I know. His books – he's had twenty-one published under his own name and fourteen under Alexander Kent – are always full of action which often takes place against an unusual background. His latest novel certainly lives up to this description as it is set in the Black Sea in 1943, a theatre of naval warfare I'm sure no other British writer has covered. It's called Torpedo Run *and the extract I've chosen from it is when the leader of the flotilla of British MTBs, which has been sent to support the Russian Navy in the area, is suddenly attacked while returning to base. It is typical Reeman: authentic and dramatic.*

Devane jerked upright as a voice yelled from the bridge, '*Aircraft!* Aircraft bearing red four-five! Angle of sight one-five!'

The alarm bells jangled throughout the boat, and Devane ran for the ladder, his mind frozen and stopped like a watch as he waited for the game to begin.

Covers were ripped from the muzzles, which were still blackened from the night's fighting. Hatches and doors were slammed shut, and men groped for ammunition or jammed themselves firmly into their gun-shields and harnesses.

Seymour was training his binoculars over the screen. Without lowering them he said, 'Two, sir. Look like Ju 88s.'

230

The boatswain's mate said, 'All guns closed up, sir.'

Devane watched the two black silhouettes. So small, so slowly confident as they banked right over to reveal their twin engines and caught the sunlight on their cockpit covers.

Devane said, 'Tell the engine room what's happening. These beauties will take a good look at us first. But I'll lay odds they're calling up their chums right now.'

He added, 'Better move the wounded man to the wardroom. He'll have a bit more protection over his head.'

Pellegrine swung the spokes and cursed as the hull tried to drag the bows off course.

'Not to bother, sir. He's bought it.'

Devane rubbed his eyes and then searched for the two Junkers again. *Bought it*. So easily said. In England there would be another heartbreak, another telegram and, hopefully, a sympathetic letter.

He thought suddenly of the silent women in the hotel. Waiting for their husbands' medals.

No wonder Whitcombe had planned for the extra crew members.

'Here they come.' Devane wheeled round. 'They'll close from starboard. Stand by all guns!'

The two aircraft had settled down on a shallow approach and were wafer-thin above the water as they turned towards the slow-moving MTB.

God, how long they were taking. Devane heard cocking levers being pulled and the starboard machine-gunner whistling through his teeth as he depressed both barrels to hold the enemy in his crosswires.

Devane said, 'Get up forrard, David, and supervise the six-pounder crew.'

Once more their eyes met. Seymour did not need to be told why. Devane was sending him from the bridge in case the whole bunch of them were wiped out to leave the boat without an officer or a coxswain.

Devane studied the oncoming aircraft until his eyes watered. Coming out of the sun, as they always did. How many more

231

times was he going to cross swords with them, he wondered? The Ju 88 had a formidable reputation as a fighter, a bomber and recce aircraft all in one.

As the planes drew closer they appeared to accelerate. Devane held his breath as the cannon and machine-guns stabbed out from the leader. He saw the shells and bullets flailing the sea like whips, then tensed as steel whimpered overhead and a great shadow roared above the mast, the twin engines deafening as the plane pulled up and away in a steep climb.

'*Open fire!*'

The Oerlikons, already trained to port, sent two lines of tracer searing after the aircraft, then swung round again as the second attacker tore towards them.

'Hard a-starboard!'

Painfully the MTB slewed round, the six-pounder hammering violently as if to outpace the machine-guns on either side of the bridge.

'Midships! Port fifteen! *Steady!*'

Devane had to stop himself from cringing as the Junkers 88 roared overhead, its pilot momentarily off balance because of their zigzag turn. He thought he saw smoke from the enemy's belly, and guessed the six-pounder had found a target. But these planes could take a lot of punishment. Devane knew that from long and bitter experience.

The aircraft were dividing, one climbing slowly, the other turning in a wide circle almost brushing the water. Devane saw the black crosses on the wings, could even imagine the thoughts of the two pilots. The MTB was alone but apparently not disabled.

Aloud he said, 'They'll come in from bow and beam. Just to test us. Hold your fire until the last hundred yards.'

He tore his eyes from the two black silhouettes and looked along his command. Gaunt, unshaven faces, red-rimmed eyes. The feverish light of battle. Toughened hands which had once wielded pens in an office or school, or had served bread to chatty housewives, like Carroll, who was now helping a lookout to drag more ammunition to the machine-guns. These were his men. Men their mothers and wives, sweethearts and friends would never see.

He saw Orel and his interpreter carrying a sub-machine-gun to the rear of the bridge and wondered where they had found it. Probably discarded by the soldiers when they had swarmed ashore, a million years ago.

Forward, squatting down behind the gun-layer and his mate, Seymour was pointing towards the low-flying Junkers. No, his parents would certainly not recognize *him*, the dreamer, the would-be writer.

Devane let the glasses drop to his chest as the two planes started their run-in, dividing the MTB's defences by their varied heights and bearings.

And what of me? She had wanted to hear from him. What was it really like?

'*Here come the bastards!*'

Seymour was yelling, 'Hold your fire! Easy, *easy!*' Like a man calming an excited horse.

'*Open fire!*'

The guns hammered into life, the tracers streaking away and crisscrossing the aircraft like a vivid web.

Brrrrrrrrrrrrrr! Brrrrrrrrrrrrrr!

Splinters cracked and thudded across the hull, and a shell ripped through the flag locker and exploded above the side deck. Devane saw Carroll puff out his cheeks and Pellegrine tug his battered cap more tightly across his slitted eyes as if to get better control of the wheel.

The six-pounder purred round and bracketed the second aircraft as it thundered across the sky, its great wings making it look like a bird of prey about to snatch them from the sea.

Brrrrrrrrrrrrrr!

More bullets and cannon shells ripped across the hull, and Devane saw a hole appear in the gratings within inches of his seaboot.

'Cease firing!'

Devane tore at his collar and wiped his face and throat with a piece of rag. The two attackers were turning away, like conspirators, as they prepared for another run.

Devane shouted, 'Report damage and casualties! More magazines, lively there!'

Men came from their stiff attitudes and stumbled to obey his commands. There was not one of them on deck who was older than twenty-five, and most were nineteen or thereabouts. But as they readjusted their gun-sights and dragged at magazines and belts they responded like old men.

Devane licked his lips. They felt like parchment. Two more attacks like the last one, maybe just one, and they had had it. It was like fighting a tiger with an umbrella.

He saw the seaman called Irwin tying a bandage on Orel's wrist, and the port machine-gunner playing with a crucifix which hung from his identity disc.

We're all equal here. So equal we'll be nothing in a few more minutes.

Devane shouted, 'Keep at it, lads. Wear the bastards down!'

It made him want to hide his face as he watched their efforts to rally to his words.

A thumbs-up from one, a broad grin from the six-pounder gun-layer, the tough leading hand from Manchester. Even Pellegrine was looking at him and nodding.

Carroll said in a hushed voice, 'Engine room, sir.'

Devane crossed to the voicepipe in two strides. So they were not even to have that last chance, that impossible gesture which had seen the end of so many battles.

'Yes?'

Ackland called, 'I can give you fifteen knots, sir.' He must have taken Devane's silence for disappointment. 'On all three shafts.'

Devane dimly heard the rising note of the aircraft as they turned towards the MTB once again. 'Thanks, Chief. Bloody well done. And they say there are no more miracles.'

Ackland sounded confused. 'Sir?'

'Never mind, Chief. Give me all you've got, *right now!*' He snapped down the cover. 'Hard a-starboard, Swain!' He felt the deck rising to the added thrust even as the wheel went over. '*Steady!*'

234

The leading Junkers seemed to swerve away as the MTB's wake broadened out on either beam in a rich white furrow. Fifteen knots was not much compared with nearly forty, but after their slow acceptance of the repeated attacks it felt like a new heart in the boat.

'On the first aircraft! *Fire!*'

Devane clung to the jerking bridge and watched every weapon which would bear, even Orel's short-range Tommy gun as it cracked out in unison.

Maybe the enemy pilot imagined the MTB had been shamming, although at these speeds it was hard to think clearly about anything. But Devane had seen the darker line in the plane's belly, the bomb bay doors wide open to put an end to the impudent boat once and for all. Their sudden increase of speed, made more impressive by the churned wash astern, must have unnerved the German enough to make him change his approach.

Devane saw the ripple of flashes along the fuselage, the sprouts of bright fire from one engine as the cannon shells smashed into the exposed belly and wing like a fiery claw. Then the plane exploded, blasted apart by her own bombs.

One second it was still there, filling the sky, and the next there was a solid ball of fire. Devane could feel the force of the explosion and its consuming heat until the fragments were scattered across the sea and only the drifting smoke remained.

The other Junkers came in fast and low, but the attack was at arm's length, with only the machine-guns spitting through the drifting pall above their consort's remains.

A few bullets hit the hull and some whined overhead, then the Junkers altered course away from them and did not turn back.

Leading Signalman Carroll was training his glasses towards the starboard bow and exclaimed huskily, 'Here come the cavalry! No wonder the buggers made off!'

Devane clung to the screen and listened to the vague throb of aircraft growing stronger and stronger. Sorokin had kept his word. They had made it.

He stared at his hands on the bridge rail, mesmerized by the red streak he had left on the grey paint with his fingers.

Seymour pounded up the ladder and stopped as he saw the shock on Carroll's face. Then he ran across the bridge and caught Devane in his arms as he lost his grip and began to fall.

For a few seconds they stood like statues, words pointless, as three pairs of Russian fighters screamed overhead in pursuit of the Junkers.

Then Seymour said, 'Help me with the captain! He's hit!'

Gales in the Southern Ocean

(From *My Lively Lady*)

Alec Rose is one of those remarkable men whose essential modesty and straightforward character is reflected strongly in his writing. You know that when he is describing an unpleasant situation, as he is in this extract, from his book, My Lively Lady, *he is probably understating the prevailing conditions. He also has a nice wry sense of humour which gave me added enjoyment when I read his book, which is about his single-handed circum-navigation in 1967/68. Originally, he'd intended to make a race of it with Francis Chichester, but a series of misfortunes prevented this. His voyage took 318 days and he put into port twice, Australia by design and New Zealand after being damaged in a storm. On his return he was knighted. He was born in 1908, so what made his circumnavigation even more remarkable was that he was nearly sixty when it took place, an age when most men are thinking of retiring from the world, not sailing around it!*

October 25th found me fighting a north-easterly gale, force 8 to 9, obliging me to lower the reefed mainsail. It was hectic for a few minutes when the shackle connecting the main halyard to the mainsail got caught in the jib halyard up aloft, and I couldn't get the mainsail down. It flogged about for some minutes, before I could free it, breaking a batten and tearing two mast slides off. We carried on under spitfire staysail. We had had these easterlies for two weeks now, and I began to wonder where those westerlies, that are supposed to blow constantly round the roaring forties, had got to.

The next day it eased enough for me to replace the broken batten and to re-seize the slides to the mainsail.

It was bitterly cold and I had three sweaters on. The wind backed to the north-west on 27 October in the early hours of the morning and I had to dress in oilskins to go aft and adjust the self-steering gear. We were running under trysail and spitfire staysail with the wind increasing. Dawn showed a wintry scene with a wild boisterous sea causing us to roll heavily. Low, heavy clouds swept by. By midday it was gale force 8, but we managed to hold onto the trysail and spitfire staysail, running at from 5 to 6 knots, in the right direction. The glass was still falling and during the afternoon hail and sleet squalls descended on us, laying us well down. Dirty-looking clouds blew up from windward.

What a cruel night that was. The darkness could be felt. A flash of white would show up as a white-crested wave ranged up alongside. Hail, sleet, rain, and cold – the worst night I had experienced. As usual, the sea won, and I was forced to lower the trysail in a fierce hailstorm biting at the skin on my face and wind force 12 shrieking and tearing at me in the pitch blackness. The same thing happened an hour later when I was forced to lower the staysail; the sail flogging and shaking the mast and the ship. I thanked God for the dawn, but that only showed up the wild wintry scene – visibility down to fifty yards and the deck white with hail and sleet.

I wondered if I had carried on too long with sail. What is the borderline between being bold and daring and being foolish and silly? This was a desolate part of the ocean, and it would have been silly to have carried something important away at that stage.

I retired below to a hot drink. As everything was damp I lit the Tilley heater, and it was warm and comfortable. All hell was let loose outside, and it continued all that day until next morning, when it eased and I got under way with reefed mainsail, spitfire staysail, and working jib.

It was still squally and there was a lumpy sea, which at one time threw me across the cockpit onto a sheet winch, bruising my ribs. I had to watch constantly as the wind would die away to force 2 and then increase to force 6 or 7 suddenly, sending me scrambling to the sheets.

I found the cross-link between the latch gear and the servo tiller, carrying the ball joint, broken off that morning. This was serious and I wondered how I could repair it. I got the gear inboard and took the broken pieces off. It was a hollow tube. I found a piece of brass rod that just went in with a driving fit. I cut it down and joined the two ends together, and it was stronger than before.

The self-steering gear is set for a certain wind strength to hold the yacht on course and with a sudden great change in wind strength it cannot do this. That night I had to scramble out constantly to hold the tiller myself in the blackness that could be felt and the deck running with water. One has practically to live in oilskins as it is impossible to go into the cockpit to empty the gash bucket without them.

November 1st was a sunny day with wind down to force 1 or 2, but a big and irregular sea was running and I had the genoa up – boomed out – and the mizzen staysail – but the sea rolled us over and threw the wind out of the sails. Nothing is ever right is it? I hoped for a few days' fine weather with a fair breeze to catch up a bit of time. There was still about 4000 miles to go, and when I thought of that and the fact that it was 2000 miles back to Africa, I was careful about the gear. I was on my own – with no radio contact – and to carry away sails or gear would be serious. So although I sailed the yacht constantly at the best we could do in the conditions, and occasionally carried on too long, I didn't think it wise – good seamanship – or fair on my own strength to take undue risks. To arrive properly and in condition was the thing I aimed at.

It was gale after gale and the night of 5 November saw the wind get up to force 7 then force 8. We were running under boomed-out jib and I hung onto it too long. The yacht was almost overwhelmed and I had a hectic time getting the sail down and disconnected from the boom. The roar of the wind, the whine in the rigging, the hiss of the sea, the spray coming over, made so much noise that no one could hear me singing 'Onward Christian Soldiers'. I couldn't even hear it myself, and

I could see nothing in the pitch blackness.

At dawn I was surveying the forlorn scene of the endless succession of waves, when I was startled by the sight of a huge whale surfaced right alongside me. He was vast and had a mottled grey look of age about him. He blew and I got the scent of him. He lay in the trough of the big seas and I thought of his great strength and power – symbolic of the wild, cruel Southern Ocean. Only he could meet it on equal terms, I thought as he dived and disappeared.

Later in the morning the sun came out. What a difference that makes! I set the boomed-out storm jib on one side and boomed-out working jib on the other and with a west-northwest wind we were making good progress at 6 knots. White-capped seas followed us up astern. It was a quiet night and *Lively Lady* ran on while I had a good sleep. I had my last apple. The last few had started going soft, but I didn't throw away many. Oranges, lemons, and grapefruit were still good, also the onions. I ate the green shoots with biscuits and cheese, followed by honey, butter, and biscuits and a good slice of cake for supper.

'Well, there was one chap who knew what it was all for, but unfortunately he left us to fly Concordes.' (From *Sod's Law of the Sea* by Bill Lucas and Andrew Spedding)

R.W. CHANDLER

Breakdown

(From *Sparks at Sea*)

Life at sea between the two great wars was far from cosy as this extract from R.W. Chandler's Sparks at Sea *shows. The recession caused large numbers of ships to be laid up, jobs were few, and shipowners scrimped and saved where they could. Chandler went to sea as a radio operator – a 'sparks' as they were affectionately called – because his poor eyesight made it impossible for him to be a deck officer. But he was a keen observer of life on board the cooperatively owned Welsh tramp ship, which must have been as spartan as you could find anywhere, and I can well appreciate his evocative description, reprinted below, of the breakdown to the ship's steering as twenty years ago I was involved in a similar incident. We were off Cape Guardafui when a cracked cylinder liner in the main engine brought us to a standstill. It took our engineers nearly twenty-four hours to replace it, a far from easy task with a three-ton lump of metal to remove, and a replacement to fit. Fortunately, we had fine weather, which is more than Chandler had, and he gives a very clear picture of the risks run, and the bravery of the seamen, fifty years ago.*

I was to go to Barry to sign on a ship called the *Alban* loading coal for the River Plate. In Barry they hoisted up the complete railway wagon in a gantry and then emptied it down a shoot into the ship's hold. The *Alban* was almost down to her marks, but she was almost invisible in a dense cloud of coaldust.

She was a typical three-island tramp of the First World War era, with a black funnel and stone-coloured upperworks. I

241

found the mate in a tiny cabin in the midship house and introduced myself as the radio operator. He took a key off a board, and with a strong Welsh accent said he would show me my accommodation. I followed him out onto the main deck, where he climbed up a ladder on a big ventilator and stopped outside the door of a tiny wooden hut behind the engine-room skylight. He opened the door; along one bulkhead was a bunk covered with filthy bedclothes, and on the other was a bench with a quarter kw spark transmitter and a receiver. I looked on in horror.

'Where's the chair, then?' I asked.

'You sit on the bunk to work that wireless if you want to sit down,' he answered.

'Where is the sleeping cabin, then?' I asked.

'There isn't one. You sleep on that bunk,' he replied.

I pulled aside the bedclothes, to find a dirty settee cushion underneath. I hoisted this up and lifted a board and there were the radio batteries. I could almost feel the hostility from the Welsh mate.

'What's wrong then, man?' he asked.

I realized that it was no good talking to him. 'I'm off to see the shipping master,' I replied, and off I went.

I had a long wait in the shipping office, but the shipping master listened patiently, and at last he said: 'Just a minute, I'll get the surveyor.' He returned a few minutes later with a tough-looking character with a strong Scots accent, who also listened to my story.

'That bloody *Alban* again, nothing but trouble from that rust bucket. It's illegal for you to sleep in the same cabin as charging batteries. I'll come down to the ship with you and sort it out.'

We were met at the gangway by the mate, but the surveyor brushed him aside and climbed onto the lower bridge with me in tow. He banged on a door and walked in, and then I met 'Old Dai', the captain of the *Alban*. The mate must have warned him that I was out for trouble, for he didn't even look at me.

'This man has been slipped a fast one,' said the surveyor. 'Let's have the ship's plans and if there's any bloody argument

242

you don't get your sailing papers.'

The plans were produced with ill grace by Old Dai, and, after glancing at them for a few minutes, the surveyor pointed with a stubby finger at the plan. 'There's a cabin in the midship house labelled Wireless Operator. Who the hell's got that?'

'That's the fourth mate's room now,' said Old Dai.

'Four mates on this bloody heap?' snarled the surveyor. 'I can't turn him out but if the radioman is to sleep in the radio room you will have to build a box outside for his batteries and then run new cables out to it. You don't get your papers until it's done and I have inspected it. It will take at least two days.'

So I got my cabin on the *Alban*.

I went into the saloon for supper that night and had a foretaste of what the trip was going to be like. The captain, Old Dai, was there, as was the first mate, always known as Yantow, the third mate, and the chief engineer. Only the last was not Welsh; he came from the north-east coast. The conversation was carried on in Welsh, but the chief engineer spoke English. 'Come up to the chain locker tonight with me, Sparks,' he invited. I accepted and over a few pints the chief introduced me to my new ship.

'She was bought by the inhabitants of a small Welsh town on the share principle in the palmy days immediately after the last war when freights were booming,' he said. 'The principal share-holder is a character they call "Jones the Goat". Old Dai has a lot of the shares and so does Yantow's father. They have kept her running until now by cutting all the corners and employing people from the home town at cut rates. The skipper feeds the ship, if you can call it feeding, and buys all the deck and engine stores. It's a miracle they can keep her running in these hard times. I have to calculate the coal to the last shovelful.'

He explained that Yantow was related to the skipper, the third mate was the skipper's cousin and the deck crew were all from villages in the same valley as Old Dai. The second mate was a very old man who had been a captain in Chellews for years but had lost his ship, and the chief was of the opinion that desperate for a job he had signed on for 1s a month as second mate just for his food. The chief said that the *Alban* was taking a cargo of coal to Rosario and was then going to Santa Fé to load maize for Japan, round the Cape of Good Hope.

That night I had a long think, for the chief had told me that the fourth mate, who had ejected me from my cabin, was Old Dai's son, just out of his apprenticeship, and that he had failed his second mate's licence. I was going to be as popular as the proverbial pork chop in a synagogue, and it was going to be a long long time before we got back to the Bristol Channel. I weighed my chances: the union would do nothing, the radio company had not forced me to sign on, but I had signed the ship's articles for a two-year voyage and I was stuck with it.

The next morning before breakfast the steward knocked on the door to inform me that the captain had said I was to attend only the second serving of meals, which would solve the problem of speaking Welsh, for the second mate, with whom I should be eating, came from Bedfordshire. Later the chief engineer joined us and still later on the fourth mate, who had served his apprenticeship in a Scots cargo boat. He had become 'bloody fed up with his old man and Yantow and their bloody Welsh' – six months with them and he wouldn't remember any English. He bore no illwill over the episode of the cabin – his moving into it had been entirely Yantow's idea when he had been sent back to sea for six months and Old Dai had agreed to sign him on as unpaid fourth mate. The chief had signed on his own crew, both the donkeyman and the fireman being Arabs who had sailed with him for years. Most of them had white wives and lived in the Loudon Square area of Cardiff.

We sailed in the middle of a pouring wet night on what was to be a long and unhappy voyage. The Welsh crew members cut themselves off entirely from the chief, the second mate and myself, but we formed our own community and lived our own lives. I remember once asking the chief what the *Alban* stood for,

'Is it the name of some aunt of the owners?' I asked.

The old second mate answered: 'Is it hell. I think she was originally called the *Albany* and had brass letters on her counter to prove it. One day the Y of Albany fell off, but they were too bloody mean to buy a new brass Y and fit it, so she became the *Alban*.' True or false, I don't know, but she was the most parish-rigged ship I was ever to sail in.

Two days after passing Land's End the *Alban* ran into a heavy south-westerly gale in which she wallowed with a heavy sodden pitching motion. The decks were continually filled with water, which came over the fo'c's'le head, though the second mate and the chief did not seem much concerned at dinner.

'She's always a cow when she's deep loaded in any sort of sea, like a half tide rock.'

The second mate had spent all his early years in sail. 'This isn't a ship,' he claimed. 'You should have seen my old ship, the *Springburn*; she'd have been boiling along to the westward with water over the lee-rail halfway up her hatches.'

The chief and I were getting used to stories of the old boy's career in sailing ships.

'Yes, all hands up to their ass in water and hanging on to their lives for a few dry biscuits,' said the chief.

'At least we had fresh meat for the first week out,' replied the second mate, and had no answer. The fresh meat had been cooked and hung on the foremast stays, a common practice in this class of ship. 'All the fresh meat went in my watch,' continued the second. 'Shipped a green one over the fo'c's'le that put solid water up to the cross trees, and, when it had drained off, all the meat had gone.'

The chief was indignant. 'Can't see why Old Dai doesn't put her head to sea and heave to until this blows itself out. Deep as she is, the props are out of the water half the time. The second and I are shutting her down each time her ass comes out of the drink to stop her shaking her guts out.'

I suggested that perhaps Old Dai had a charter to catch in Santa Fé.

'We'll catch a bloody harp apiece to play on Fiddlers Green if he keeps her pounding into this lot,' was the chief's comment.

Back in the wildly swinging radio cabin I wedged myself on the bunk and listened to the 600-m traffic. There was a voice-pipe connection to the bridge through which I passed the information that winds of gale force were being forecast by Land's End, Ushant and Vigo. The news was received without comment by the bridge; 'The Eisteddfod', as the chief had christened them, weren't impressed. Just as I was going off watch at 10 p.m., the *Alban* gave a heavy lurch to port and then slowly rolled over until the list must have been 45°. I climbed out into the pitch black night. The *Alban* had turned beam on and was wallowing in the trough of a high confused sea. I heard the clang of the telegraph and then the comforting thump of the old steam engine died away. I climbed down the ventilator ladder and dashed along the engine-room alleyway. The steam steering engine was on the top engine-room platform at the after end and was surrounded by people.

The chief lifted a white face, streaked with grease, and saw me. 'One of the steering chains gave, Sparkie. This may be your chance to send an SOS.'

The donkeyman had rigged up a cargo light cluster and the after-deck was now illuminated – and a wild sight it was. The ship was rolling heavily and at the bottom of each roll she scooped up a huge sea, which roared across to the other side as she rolled back. The hatch was covered with a roaring cataract of water.

The chief was angry. 'Don't talk rubbish, you Welsh bastard,' he yelled at Yantow. 'The steering engine's all right, it's the chains on the port side running back to the quadrant that have carried away.' The *Alban* had the old type steering gear, a combination of chains on the poop and rods along the afterdeck. The poop, as well as the afterdeck, was being continually swept by heavy water and somewhere under it was a break in the steering gear.

The fourth mate now jumped into the breach. Picking his time between seas he scooted across No. 4 hatch, using the stowed derrick guys for a handrail, and climbed onto the poop. A sea roared over the poop and I lost him; when it cleared he was still there hanging onto the rails. He stumbled around waist deep for a while and then dashed back across the hatch to the engine room again. He ignored us all except the chief.

246

The chief and second engineers now went into a conference in the chief's cabin, and, when they returned, the chief gave his decision.

'The second and I can turn up a new bolt and nut, but it will take six hours, and then we have to fit it again; it's going to be a long job. I think you ought to have a tug standing by. We are taking a hell of a pounding and, if a hatch cover tears off, we're done.'

Old Dai didn't like it one bit. 'You make the bolt, chief, and I'll look after the ship. If a tug gets a wire on us, it'll cost the earth.'

'The earth!' shouted the chief. 'The old cow won't be worth a plugged nickel if a hatch goes.'

I climbed back into the radio room and listened out on 600 m to pass the night away. I then found that there was another ship in trouble, an Italian further down the Bay; she had sent out a call for help and the French tug *Albeille III* from Brest was steaming to her position. I told Yantow over the voice pipe that the big tug was going to pass near our position.

'Never mind the tug, man. You mind your own bloody business,' was his only reaction.

The night wore on – the rolling seemed to get worse but it was probably only my imagination – and the dawn found us wet and tired, with the chief and second still struggling with the new bolt. It was ready by midday, and, accompanied by Yantow and the fourth mate, they made the perilous journey to the poop. With block and tackle they hauled the chain and the rod close and slipped in their new bolt. Working on that rolling deck and continually up to their waists in water, they were unable to finish the job before dark.

But the new bolt held, and the old *Alban* was slowly brought round until the sea was just off her bow, and there she remained hove-to for two days until the sea eased enough for us to proceed with the voyage.

I asked the chief afterwards what Old Dai had said about that wild night and day's work.

'Nothing really. The second and I went to see him after we

247

were hove-to and suggested a drink to thaw us out.'

'You know I don't approve of strong drink, man. I'll get the cook to make some coffee.'

'We refused,' said the chief. 'Apparently, as well as being the meanest old sod I have ever sailed with, he also belongs to some Holy Joe outfit that don't drink.'

A Galley's Day

(From *Naval Occasions*)

'Bartimeus' was the pen-name of a naval captain called Ritchie who wrote during and after the First World War. He wrote dozens of books about the Navy – my favourite is Middle Watch *– and he carved quite a reputation for himself which still lingers on. He also wrote short pieces – several of which appeared in the famous* Blackwood's Edinburgh *magazine, now unhappily defunct – and it is one of these, from his book,* Naval Occasions, *that I've chosen as it mirrors so well a time gone for ever. But his characters are as true today as they were sixty or seventy years ago.*

Boom! On board the flagship a puff of smoke rose and dissolved in the breeze; the cluster of whalers and gigs that had been hovering about the starting line sped away before the wind. The bay to windward resembled the shallows near the nesting ground of white-winged gulls as the remaining gigs, whalers, and cutters zigzagged tentatively to and fro, and a couple of belated 25-foot whalers, caught napping, went tearing down among them.

The launches and pinnaces do not start for another hour, and are for the most part still at the booms of their respective ships. There are three more classes before us, and it only remains to keep out of the way and an eye on the stop watch. The breeze is freshening, and it looks like a 'Galley's day'. A 32-foot cutter (handiest and sweetest of all Service boats to sail) goes skimming past on a trial run. Her gilded badge gleams in the spray, and there is a sheen of brasswork and enamel about her that proclaims the pampered darling of a ship. The midshipman at the helm – to show a mere galley what he can do – chooses a squall in which he put her about; she spins around like a top, and is off on her new tack in the twinkling of an eye.

Casey, petty officer and captain's coxswain, is busy forward with the awning and an additional halliard rove through a block at the foremast head. This, steadied by the boathook, will serve us as a spinnaker during the three-mile run downwind; and, in a Service rig race, is the only additional fitting allowed beyond what is defined as 'the rig the boat uses on service, made of service canvas by service labour'.

Only half a minute now. . . . Check away the sheets. Spinnaker halliards in hand.

Boom! We are off! Hoist spinnaker!

As we cross the line the 32-foot cutter and a couple of gigs slip over abreast of us; astern a host of white sails come bellying in our wake; up to windward the pinnaces and launches are manoeuvring for positions. The cutter has 'goose-winged' her dipping lug and is running dead before the wind. In a narrow boat like a galley this is dangerous and does not pay. Luffing a little, we get the wind on our quarter, and the gigs follow suit. Presently the cutter gybes and loses ground; the gigs, too, have dropped astern a little.

Our galley's crew settle down in the bottom of the boat, and producing pipes and cigarettes from inside their caps, speculate on the chances of the day. Far ahead the smaller fry are negotiating the mark buoy. Imperceptibly the breeze freshens, till the wind is whipping a wet smoke off the tops of the waves. Casey, tending the mainsheet, removes his pipe and spits overside. 'I reckons we'll want our weatherboards before we'm done, sir,' he prophesies. We have shown the rest of our class a clean pair of heels by now, and are fast overhauling the whalers. At last the mark buoy.

'Down spinnaker!' and round we go, close hauled. Now the work starts. A white squall tearing down the bay blinds us with spray and fine desert sand. The water pours over the gunwale as we luff and luff again. There's nothing for it: we must reef, and while we do so, round come the remainder, some reefed and labouring, others lying up in the wind with flapping sails. A nasty short sea has set in, and at the snub of each wave, the galley, for all the careful nursing she receives, quivers like a sensitive being.

'She can't abear that reef in her foresail,' says Casey; 'it do make her that sluggish.' As he spoke, our rival, the 32-foot cutter, went thrashing past under full sail, her crew crouched to windward. It was going to be neck or nothing with them. Then, by James – 'Got anything to bail with, forward there?'

'Yessir!' replied seven voices as one.

'Stand by to shake out that reef!' We luffed for a second while two gigs and a pinnace crept up on our quarter, and then off we went in the seething wake of the cutter. Even Casey's big toe curled convulsively as he braced himself against the thwart and spat on his hands to get a fresh grip on the mainsheet. The spray hissed over us like rain, and, under cover of his oilskin, I believe No. 5, perched on the weather gunwale, was sorrowfully unlacing his boots.

'If it don't get no worse,' says Casey, 'we'll do all right.' With his bulldog chin above the gunwale he commenced a running commentary on the proceedings. '. . . 'Strewth! There's 'is foremast gorn!' He gazed astern enraptured. 'Commander's weather shroud carried away, sir, an' 'im a-drifting 'elpless. . . . Them whalers is bailin' like loo-natics –' he gave a hoarse chuckle, 'like proper loo-natics, sir. . . . That there launch precious near fouled the mark buoy. . . . 'E'll run down that gig if 'e don't watch it. Their owner sailing 'er too.'

Then the squalls died away and the breeze steadied. I could hear the surge of a launch as she came crashing along on our quarter, but once round the second mark buoy and on the port tack no one could touch us – at least so Casey vowed.

Suddenly the half-drowned bowman gave the first sign of animation that he had displayed since the green seas began to break over him. 'She's missed stays,' he announced with gruff relish, peering under the lip of the foresail.

''Oo? Not that cutter . . .?' Casey so far forgot himself as to squirt tobacco juice into the sacred bottom of his own boat. 'Yessir, an' so help me,' he added in confirmation, 'she's in Hirons!' *

The next minute we passed to windward of our rival, as with flapping sheets and reversed helm she drifted slowly astern. Her midshipman avoided our eyes as we passed, but his expression of incredulous exasperation I have seen matched only on the face of one whose loved and trusted hunter has refused a familiar jump. Above the noise of the wind and waves I heard his angry wail –

'O-o-oh! Isn't she a cow!'

The wind held fair and true, and, as Casey prophesied, it proved a Galley's day after all. A launch and two pinnaces raced us for the flagship's ram, and our rudder missed the cable by inches as we wore to bring us onto the finishing line. Even then the launch nearly had it; but I think that the observations exchanged, as we slipped round side by side (*sotto voce* and perfectly audible to every one in both boats), between Casey and the launch's coxswain, did much to spoil the nerve of the first lieutenant who was sailing her.

Much of that day I have forgotten. But the sheen of white sails sprinkled along the triangular nine-mile course, the grey hulls of the fleet against the blue of sea and sky, the tremor of the boat's frame as the water raced hissing past her clinker-built sides, the bucket and shrug, the lurch and reel and plunge as she fought her way to windward – all these things have combined to make a blur of infinitely pleasant memories.

Casey gave a sigh of contentment and handed back an empty glass through the pantry door.

'Well, sir,' he said, 'I reckon that was a proper caper!' Then, as if realizing that his summing-up of the race required adequate embellishment, and less formal surroundings in which to do the occasion justice, he wiped his mouth on the back of a huge paw and moved forward out of sight along the messdeck.

* A boat is said to be 'in irons' when she lies dead head-to-wind and cannot pay off on either tack.

"Hold your course, John, we don't want to confuse him now."
(From *Come Sailing Again* by Mike Peyton)

JOSHUA SLOCUM

Finis

(From *Sailing Alone Around the World*)

I don't think we could finish this book without putting something cheerful at the end of it, and Joshua Slocum's advice to anyone wishing to go to sea seems as appropriate today as when it was written nearly ninety years ago. So many of us who have been lucky enough to make the time for a long cruise would agree wholeheartedly with his last sentence.

To young men contemplating a voyage I would say go. The tales of rough usage are for the most part exaggerations, as also are the stories of sea danger. I had a fair schooling in the so-called 'hard ships' on the hard Western Ocean, and in the years there I do not remember having once been 'called out of my name'. Such recollections have endeared the sea to me. I owe it further to the officers of all the ships I ever sailed in as boy and man to say that not one ever lifted so much as a finger to me. I did not live among angels, but among men who could be roused. My wish was, though, to please the officers of my ship wherever I was, and so I got on. Dangers there are, to be sure, on the sea as well as on the land, but the intelligence and skill God gives to man reduce these to a minimum. And here comes in again the skilfully modelled ship worthy to sail the seas.

To face the elements is, to be sure, no light matter when the sea is in its grandest mood. You must then know the sea, and know that you know it, and not forget that it was made to be sailed over.